My Foot In The Door

Dr Ross Muir
&
Hélena Gresty

My foot
in the Door

www.myfootinthedoor.co.uk

Copyright© Quintessential Publishing Limited, 2010
Cover illustrations by Caroline Parkinson
Chapter illustrations by Daniel Vardy

First published in 2010 by
Quintessential Publishing Limited
14 Gladewood Close
Wilmslow
Cheshire SK9 2GN
United Kingdom

QUINTESSENTIAL
PUBLISHING

www.myfootinthedoor.co.uk

British Library Catalogue

A CIP catalogue record for this book is available from the British Library.

ISBN 978-0-9561224-2-1

We have attempted to be as accurate as possible with the information contained in this book at the time of going to press. However, this book is for general guidance only and cannot be regarded as a substitute for professional advice. Consequently, the author and publisher accept no liability for loss or damage of any kind, which may arise from any person relying on information contained in this book.

Printed and bound by CPI Anthony Rowe, Chippenham, Wiltshire

Authors

Ross Muir
BA VetMB MRCVS BMBCh

Ross' path into medicine was perhaps more circuitous than most as he was already five years into a degree in Veterinary Medicine at Cambridge University when he had the sudden epiphany that the one species he actually wanted to treat was the only one he was not actually qualified to. This prompted him to apply for a place on the Oxford University graduate entry medical course where he studied for four years while working part time as a vet (which did at times cause inter-species confusion though he is yet to approach a human patient with shoulder-length gloves). He has now been a qualified doctor for two years and is currently on a surgical training scheme in the Oxford Radcliffe Hospitals NHS trust. When not working towards a career in reconstructive surgery or scheming how to add more letters after his name he is most likely to be found masquerading as a triathlete, cycling lots, running a bit and swimming only when really, absolutely necessary.

"I would like to thank Chris for being endlessly patient with our inability to reply to emails and ever flexible with deadlines. Thanks to everyone who added colour and interest to the book with the profiles they provided, and to our Caroline Parkinson for the fantastic illustrations. Finally I'd like to thank Ruth for being there to bounce ideas off and for being the only person who didn't think I was completely mad for going back to school to study medicine."

Heléna Gresty BA

H eléna is in her final year of studying medicine at the University of Oxford. She is interested in pursuing a career in Acute Medicine and completed an intercalated BA degree in Medical Science, focusing on cardiovascular medicine with research into early murine cardiac embryology. She was happy to receive offers from all four medical schools she applied to and has been a member of the interviewing panel for Merton College, Oxford. In her free time she enjoys rowing and hockey as well as shopping and hanging out with her friends.

"I would like to thank our publishing team for their hard work and patience in bringing this book to fruition. I would also like to thank my tutors at Merton College, Oxford and all of our contributors. Special thanks also go to Tom and my parents. Thank you all."

Illustrators

Caroline Parkinson (Cover Graphics)

Caroline is a freelance illustrator currently based in Norwich. She graduated from Loughborough University in 2004 and has worked as an art assistant and props finder for the children's television shows "Mr Maker" and "Charlie and Lola." Other projects include the short film, "The Cloud Factory" for The Arts Council, character animation for the British Animation Awards, and several comics for various anthologies, including the British science fiction magazine 'Murky Depths' and 'Factor Fiction Press.'

More examples of Caroline's work can be found on her website *www.carolineparkinson.co.uk.*

Dan Vardy (Chapter Graphics)

Dan Vardy trained as a Graphic Designer at Solent University. After having a year out as a Church Youth Worker, working in an Orphanage and running youth events, he worked as a Graphic Designer. This involved designing items ranging from leaflets to Shop Front displays. After some time in this role he was drawn back to work with young people and became a Graphics/ Art Teacher. He currently works in a school in Southampton.

Contents

Preface

This book is both an inspiration and a guide. All readers will experience the authors' excitement and enthusiasm about medicine but those who are uncertain whether it is the right career choice can use this book to help in making a well informed and dispassionate decision. One of the key messages, however, is that there is so much variation within medicine that it is in effect a gateway to a thousand different careers.

This book is also for those who are clear that they want to apply to medical school, and, for them, it provides the best guidance for preparation that I know. In order to ensure that the advice they give is sound the authors have talked to experienced and senior doctors across many fields, and to people involved in the admission process. They have also taken advice from junior doctors and students. But what makes the book so helpful, and unique, is that it has been written by those who have recently and successfully applied to med school themselves. These authors have firsthand experience of what it is like to be in your position and they know what will help you. The list of possible interview questions, for example, and the advice given are extraordinarily comprehensive, thorough and wise.

It is not possible, and perhaps not desirable, to prepare for every question, and some cannot be predicted. My wife applied to Oxford. The first stage in the medical course was known as *physiological sciences*. At interview my wife was asked: why did you spell *medicine* wrongly on your application form? She is somewhat dyslexic and had spelt it *medicine*. She gave the truthful reply: 'I knew that I couldn't possibly spell *physiological sciences*'. She came out of that interview convinced that she would be rejected. As it turned out she was wrong. It is never easy, and seldom worth, predicting the outcomes of interviews.

There are some jobs and professions that act as conversation stoppers. Medicine is not one of them. Quite the contrary. If you say you are a doctor, at a party for example, there is immediate interest. Doctors matter to people. If you become a doctor you will be able to help others at difficult times in their lives. The interest may not always be what you expect and perhaps not always what you want. Shortly after I began my training in psychiatry I went on a week's residential painting course held in a large Victorian house. The ten of us on the course gathered on the first evening in the drawing room. We exchanged brief accounts of what we did. It was like the beginning of a 1930's country house murder mystery. I told the other residents that I was a psychiatrist. Over that week almost everyone on the course took me aside at some stage to ask my advice about either their own problems or those of close relatives. As a doctor one is often guardian to other people's secrets.

Good instruction should be fun. The content of *Med School* is authoritative but the style is relaxed. Here is a guide, for all those who are giving medicine at least some consideration, that you can trust and also whose company you will enjoy. I thoroughly recommend it.

Tony Hope

Professor of Medical Ethics at the University of Oxford Medical School
Honorary Consultant Psychiatrist
Founding co-author of the Oxford Handbook of Clinical Medicine

Chapter 1

Why Medicine?

So, why do you want to be a doctor? This classic question will be asked of you hundreds of times at all stages of the application process and throughout your career. Why do you *really* want to be a doctor? It is surely an important question to ponder before launching yourself into studying medicine.

Maybe you have a burning desire to perform open-heart surgery, or perhaps help treat HIV in remote Africa. Alternatively, perhaps the quiet life as a General Practitioner (GP) in the countryside, or working at a big teaching hospital is what attracts you. Of course, studying this subject does not necessarily mean you want or have to end up as a doctor. Maybe you envisage using your medical degree to practice medical law or work in the pharmaceutical industry. We could very easily spend this entire book discussing the variety of career options that a medical degree offers. The important point to emphasise is that medicine as a degree opens up a vast and varied landscape of opportunities for those who study it. Having an appreciation of this variety will certainly enhance your application but also make you realise that it is perfectly acceptable to change your mind whilst on the journey! It is widely agreed that a degree in medicine equips its graduates with a solid scientific education and skills for pretty much any job you can think of, from engineering to journalism to banking.

1.1 What motivates *you* to be a doctor?

Well, usually there is an element of wanting to help people. Does this apply to you? Yes? Good. Being a doctor puts you in a unique position in which someone you have never met before will show and tell you

4

intimate details about themselves that they have never told anyone else. This is a real privilege and it should be treated with respect. You will experience the extremes of life from the joy of birth to a person's death, so people skills are essential. Having a talent at being able to communicate well with patients is a huge advantage and can make a substantial impact on patient care. For example, you may be the one person a patient feels comfortable approaching with a distressing and embarrassing symptom like rectal bleeding. This could result in your being able to diagnose their rectal cancer whilst it is still at a treatable stage.

Of course, the nature of this work means that working as a doctor can be both physically and mentally exhausting. You must be prepared for this and be able to talk about how you deal with stress and also how you like to relax. Throughout the application process medical schools will be looking for your ability to empathise and your interest in people, so even if this is not your primary motivation you need to show it somewhere. However, if you don't feel the emotional connection you make with patients is your primary motivator, do not be dismayed. There is a certain amount of communication skill you will require and which will be tested at interview, but many consultant medics and surgeons went into medicine for other reasons and the NHS would be a lot worse off without them. Some people are particularly interested in the intricate functioning of the human body and the ways in which we can alter this to treat disease. For example, anaesthetists get the bulk of their contact with patients as they sleep. Much of their time is spent monitoring the data from machines and administering drugs as well as liaising with the surgeon. That said, people need to be able to place absolute trust in the person that is putting them off to sleep, so the time anaesthetists spend with their conscious patients is crucial. Without anaesthetists, the aforementioned person with rectal cancer could not have it surgically removed. Essentially, the point is that so long as you are not dangerously antisocial, there is probably an area of medicine that suits your personality and ambitions.

1.2   How do I know if medicine is for me?

The best advice to anyone who wants to ascertain whether studying and practising medicine is for them is to gather as much experience as they can to inform this decision. This may be in the form of work experience or just a chat with someone in the field. We will cover what to do about work experience in a separate chapter. Don't worry if you do not have a doctor in the family or as a friend as there should be opportunities for everyone to have access to the medical community. If this is the case you will need to be keen and almost certainly persistent in finding contacts. Talk to as many doctors, medical students and other health professionals as you can. Remember to ask questions about what studying and practising medicine involves, rather than just turning up for the sake of it. You might find it useful to think about particular character traits that make a particular health professional effective at their job, or how they work within a team to treat patients. If you are lucky enough to speak to a medical researcher try to get a basic appreciation of their work and its impact on the medical community. If you don't put in this effort you will have at best a primitive grasp of what the future may hold for you studying and practising medicine. Not only is it a bit silly to embark on a journey as a medical student without having your heart in it but it is glaringly obvious to the admissions tutors at interview.

If you get really stuck in to your work experience or are lucky enough to have a doctor in the family you will have realised that life as a doctor and a medical student is a challenge. Medical students are infamous for working and playing hard. The academic testing you will undertake is difficult, even for the brightest students, and you should expect to work hard at university. Similarly, once qualified as a junior 'foundation' doctor you will find yourself at the bottom of another ladder with, yes, more exams in your path to move upwards. You should be vaguely familiar with the progression from a foundation doctor (F1 and F2 currently totals two years) through core and specialty training to eventually become a consultant. Each step of the way will involve learning new skills and the opportunity to 'specialise' in a particular area of medicine. Even consultants are kept on their toes in this respect. This system means you will be studying for exams for a long time but, on the bright side, you will always be academically stimulated. This culture of continuing education and exams is one of the reasons that academic achievement is a major focus in the selection process for medical school - you simply can't make progress in the career without a certain amount of brains. See the 'Admissions' chapter for more information about academic requirements.

1.3 Life as a Doctor

You may have heard horror stories about the kind of hours that junior doctors have to work. Fortunately in this country the days of working 48 hour straight shifts have gone. Instead, junior doctors' hours are governed by the European Working Time Directive which, from the 1st of August 2009, has limited them to a maximum of 48 hours in a working week. In a profession where patients need care 24 hours a day this has forced a change in the way we provide medical cover to more of a shift-based system where you do your allotted hours and then hand over care of your patients to the next doctor.

That's the theory at least. In reality most of us who go into medicine are quite caring souls who tend to feel that we shouldn't leave until the job is done. It's a bit difficult to say "sorry Mrs Jones, I know you might be having a heart attack but look, its five o'clock, I'll see you in the morning." It can also be hard to avoid feeling guilty at dumping a load of work on one of your colleagues. Because of this it's certainly not unheard of for junior doctors to work beyond the hours on their rota so you'll have to be prepared to do that on occasions.

And, of course since doctors are needed 24 hours a day you will have to do your share of nightshifts and weekend shifts which can really get in the way of your social life! Although these shifts can seem very scary since there is usually a lot less help around if you do have very sick patients, they are also often the most satisfying because that's when the decisions that you can make most often can end up saving lives. If the hours and the shifts seem a bit off-putting do bear in mind that the first few years of professional life for your peers who choose to work in the City will involve working similar, if not longer, hours in jobs that are a lot less interesting!

1.4   Pay – what's it like?

At least you will be getting a decent wage for your hard work and years of study, though the way pay is calculated may seem confusing at first. At the time of print, all junior doctors in the UK in their FY1 year receive a basic salary of around £22,000 which is then multiplied by a factor (called 'salary banding') of up to 1.5 depending on the exact number of hours which your rota says you should work, how intense the work is and how 'unsociable' your hours are deemed to be (in terms of night/weekend shifts). Since you are likely to be rotating through three or four jobs in that FY1 year your pay will go up or down from one month to the next if the jobs have different salary bands. In your second year after graduation your basic salary jumps to around £27,500 and continues to make smaller jumps each year after that. There is no such thing as overtime for doctors so if you do have to stay late one evening you will not get paid extra for it. You can, however, boost your income by arranging to work extra shifts as a locum on your days off, for example, to cover for people who are off sick.

1.5   Where will I end up working?

Another thing that may impact on your decision as to whether medicine is for you is the fact that you may not be able to decide where you want to study and work straight away. Hopefully you will be fortunate enough to gain a place at your chosen medical school. However, many people do end up at perfectly good medical schools, but in an area of the country that they had not envisioned themselves. Furthermore, when you apply for your first job as a foundation doctor, you are asked to rank your choice of areas you would like to work in. You might not get your first choice, particularly in competitive regions such as London and Southern England so be prepared to be flexible in your junior years. As you move into higher training you can choose which areas you want to apply to and therefore where you live, but some specialties are more competitive than others and a compromise is needed between your choice of job and area of the country you'd like to live in.

1.6   How will people react to me?

One of the most interesting things about being a doctor is the reaction of the non-medical public to you. People in Britain today are fascinated by their bodies, how they work and what we doctors are doing to them. If you don't believe us just flick through the weekly TV guide and circle the programmes about people with bizarre deformities, embarrassing medical problems, cosmetic surgery disasters, Casualty, Holby City, Gray's Anatomy, ER, House… the list goes on and on. And if people are not being 'informed' about the medical profession by TV then there are always the tabloid newspapers to stir things up! If nothing else it means that when you are out for dinner with people from a bunch of different professions they are always far more interested in what you do in your job than what anyone else gets up to. "I took out someone's spleen today" trumps "I sat at my desk and juggled numbers on my computer" any time. The drawback is that although there is still a lot of respect for the medical profession in society, the sheer volume of misinformation and half truths in the media means that people are no longer afraid to question doctors, even criticise them, and this is something to be prepared for as you come into the profession. Your communication skills will be tested daily explaining why your course of treatment is more appropriate than Hugh Lauries'. Trust and co-operation need to be earned from your patients, it doesn't just happen by magic, and you need to be prepared for the emotions, both positive and negative, that patients and families will show towards you. Medicine is such an emotive area that people will love you, hate you, congratulate you and criticise you, though hopefully not in equal measure!

Summary

If we have not yet managed to put you off medicine as a career then there is a good chance that no one is going to be able to. In this case, grab yourself a cup of tea and a comfy seat and enjoy this book. It has been written for you by people who have been in the exact same position as you find yourself now. Be reassured that it is by no means impossible to get into medical school and by picking up this publication you are making proactive steps towards reaching your goals. Good luck and enjoy the read.

"Let the young know they will never find a more interesting, more instructive book than the patient himself."

Giorgio Baglivi

Chapter 2

Work Experience

Having some work experience is essential to gain a place at medical school. As alluded to already, it is in your best interests to have an idea of what is in store for your future, but it is also one of those hoops that you absolutely must jump through in order to gain a place. But do not fret... sorting this out is easy if you know how!

In this chapter we will give you an idea of what medical schools value in a good work experience portfolio. We will outline the basic choices you should make as well as some more original ideas and tell you what you should aim to gain from them. We will then give you some top tips on how to apply for and get a worthwhile placement. The most important point is to make the most of your time there so you can show off what you have learnt in your personal statement and at interview.

2.1   What do the Admissions Tutors want?

Admissions tutors want to see that you have a basic grasp of what is involved in being a medical student and studying medicine. Even if you envisage yourself using your medical degree to go in another direction you should play the game here and be able to talk about the life of a doctor. It looks really silly if you are planning to embark upon a career of which you know nothing about. Work experience shows the admissions tutors that you are not only well informed, but hard working and dedicated to the cause.

Admissions tutors also like variety and breadth. One of the reasons for this is that medicine, as a career, is very varied. Bearing this in mind, our best advice would be to do the minimum of some hospital and community work experience, but also something different that will make you stand out from the crowd. Within these choices you should also aim to show both a compassionate and scientific side to yourself.

2.2 Places to apply

First of all, the basics. You should try to get some experience in a hospital, in general practice and in the voluntary sector.

In this chapter we will offer some explanation of what you should aim to gain from the experience, focused around what you may be asked at interview.

Hospital

In the hospital placement you should try to talk to as many doctors as you can about their experiences and their lifestyle. Ideally, you would follow one around for a few days to get really stuck in. The essential point is that you pick out things from the experience that interest or surprise you. Admissions tutors hate it when students have obviously turned up in a hospital for the sake of it and learnt nothing!

Some potential ideas are:

1. Follow a particular patient and research their condition

2. Understand the different ways a condition can be diagnosed and treated

3. Develop an appreciation of the differing perspectives of the doctor and patient

Heléna was lucky enough to attend a radiology teaching session for junior doctors and then wrote about this experience in her personal statement. She also spent time with the doctors as they made decisions about patient care and with nurses as they implemented it.

You should likewise try to get an appreciation of the many professionals that are now involved in patient care, from doctors and nurses to occupational therapists and social workers. This is a good thing to talk about at interview and is often missed by weaker candidates.

General Practice

General practice is often a fall-back for those that are unable to gain experience in a hospital, but if you have the chance you should do both. Hospitals and general practice have lots of similarities but also many differences so, if you do both, it is something interesting to talk about at interview.

In a general practice placement you may be able to sit in with a general practitioner (GP) or nurse during their consultations. Some ideas to focus on are how the GP communicates effectively with their patients, how they identify a sick patient that needs immediate treatment and how the referral system works. You may also get an appreciation of health promotion in the community or how the vaccination schedule works.

Unfortunately lots of potential medical students waste two weeks working on the reception desk or stuffing envelopes. By all means do some admin if you are asked to help the practice out in exchange for the opportunity to learn from the doctors, but remember you must learn something from the experience overall, rather than just write it on your statement to tick a box. It might be a bit embarrassing to be asked about your experience with a GP only to be able to talk about how their snazzy photocopier works!

14

Voluntary Work

Working in the voluntary sector is a brilliant opportunity to demonstrate to the admissions tutors that you are motivated to help people and can empathise with the social impact that health has on peoples' lives.

In this aspect of your work experience you should aim to display a long term commitment to the cause, ideally a year or more. This shows that caring for people is a real part of your life and not a sudden afterthought that you had when it came to applying for university. Hopefully you will really enjoy this and be able to use your talents to help others. Lots of people work in residential homes for the elderly but you might prefer to work with disadvantaged children or people with disabilities.

Usually the fact that you have spent time doing voluntary work says a lot about your character but you should be prepared to talk about the experience at interview. Some ideas you might want to discuss are how your perspective about a particular group changed during your voluntary work, or what you learnt from the people you helped, or maybe even the importance of patience and listening skills in this sector. You will probably come up with other ideas as you go along in your placement but, again, do not turn up simply to tick a box on the admissions form!

Something Special

Once you have covered these basics you will have the chance to embellish your application and interview with what will make you stand out from the other applicants. You have the scope to choose from many possibilities so try to think of something that you will enjoy and want to learn more about.

The ideas we will talk about are by no means exhaustive. Perhaps you have the opportunity to do some aid work abroad and are able to talk about the differences in health problems and solutions in other geographical and economic environments. Some applicants expand on this idea during a gap year.

Those of you with a scientific flair may have some experience working in a laboratory or observing how a clinical trial works in a hospital setting. Heléna spent some time at the Institute of Cancer Research in a programme they run for sixth-formers. She found out about it by using contact details for job advertisements in the back of a scientific magazine. Charitable and even commercial scientific groups may offer such schemes on a year-to-year basis so drop them an email or a polite telephone call to see if they are running such a scheme. She observed the work of scientists and got the opportunity to do some tests exploring the genetic basis of cancer. Once again, what made this process worthwhile was that she tried to learn about what was happening both in the lab and its application to the pathology of cancer so she could talk about it at interview. She did some reading into the basics of cancer and some new ideas about its treatment.

This is what differentiates candidates who, on the one hand, got some experience because of a family contact and sat like a lemon for two weeks, and someone who engaged with what they were experiencing and thought about how it may affect them as a doctor in years to come.

Why do we keep going on about this 'make the most of your experience' business? The main reason is that unfortunately there is still a big disparity between applicants to medical schools in terms of the opportunities to gain experience. Some of you may have mothers and fathers who are doctors, with friends you can shadow in a hospital without much of a problem. That is a great opportunity and you should make the most of it. However, you might be the first scientist in your family and in a school with no links to a hospital. You should not be discriminated against either.

So how do admissions tutors tell those who want to tick a box from those who want to grow from their experience? How will they know if you actually worked really hard to get your one bit of work experience and that you made the very most of it? They will look for your enthusiasm, a determination to find a place when it was difficult and evidence that you have made the most of the opportunity you did have.

Other Opportunities

You may also want to have a think about taking advantage of some special schemes which aim to support and inform people who are wanting to study medicine. They range from short seminars to residential weekends. They can be a nice way to speak to others who are going through the same experience, as well as current medical students, doctors and academics. There are quite a few around, in several places across the UK.

Helena attended the Medlink course, which is held at the University of Nottingham Medical School (but not allied to it). It aims to help students decide if medicine is for them and then prepare them for a successful application. Attendees are introduced to some basic medical concepts and clinical skills as well as to other students from throughout the UK and the world. There are additional options for students looking at applying to Oxford or Cambridge and 'bolt on' extras such as a pathology course. Check out ***www.medlink-uk.org*** for more information.

There are many other schemes you may be interested in that advertise on the web. Remember that whilst many people find these courses useful and enjoyable, they are by no means a magic ticket in to medical school. If you would really like to go, but perhaps cannot afford it, get in touch with the careers organiser at your school as there may be special funding available for you. One thing to note is that, whilst such courses can be useful, they are not an alternative to gaining a good variety of work-experience.

2.3   How to apply for work experience

It is never too early to start researching work experience options and applying for them. The earlier you start the greater the number of places you will be able to have, which will hopefully give you the variety you should aim for in your application. Hopefully you will really enjoy sampling life as a doctor, but if you start your research early you will also be able to keep your options open for other career paths too. Some people leave it a bit late and do not use the experience to inform them as to whether this is the career that suits them, and then feel a bit pushed into a corner when it comes to writing their UCAS application.

So remember, work experience is as much a tool for you to decide whether you want to be a doctor as it is to enhance your application to medical school. Some people may be surprised at the level of stress that is involved when making life and death decisions or realise the working hours of a doctor would not suit them. It is better to understand this as early as possible so you do not waste your precious time at medical school.

Once you have decided which places you would like to visit for work experience it is time to get in touch with them. A good way to do this is to find out who is in charge, for example, by putting in a polite, enquiring telephone call or by looking at their website. If you are lucky enough to have a contact that works in your chosen place then they will be able to help you with this. Heléna used the advertising pages at the back of the 'New Scientist' to find websites, emails and telephone numbers to enquire through. The aim is to obtain the name of a specific person to write to as general, non-targeted letters will possibly be opened by others and may simply end up in the bin before reaching anyone with the power to offer you a placement. Your careers advisor may know who to contact at specific places so it is worth asking.

The next step is to write a nice letter to the person in charge and introduce yourself, setting out your request briefly whilst all the while appreciating that they are under no obligation to offer you a place and would be making a big effort for you. This is the crucial deal maker or breaker, because if you fail to make a favourable impression in the first few lines of the letter then it will head straight for the shredder in seconds!

There are some simple things that put people off:

1. Not constructing a letter properly

2. Spelling things incorrectly – don't rely on your computer's spellchecker as they don't always pick up errors

3. Using an incorrect title for the addressee. Surgeons are known as Mr, Miss or Mrs, rather than Dr, and do not miss if they are a Professor! Doctors are particularly fond of these names and get rather irate if they are downgraded a peg or two when spoken or written to.

It is a good idea to ask someone like a parent or teacher to read the letter and check that a mistake has not gone under the radar. You may want to ask someone who you trust for an honest opinion and get them to tell you if there is anything you could do to make it better.

Try to make sure your letter is not too long as there is a danger that the person reading it will get bored and not finish. Try to limit your letter to no more than half an A4 page. It is a nice touch to say that you look forward to hearing from them as you are more likely to get a reply, even if it is a rejection. It is common place in the job market to follow up an application a couple of days later with a courteous phone call. This demonstrates professionalism, assuming your manner in the phone call is appropriate, and also highlights your determination. The office may be very busy and they may simply have forgotten to reply to the letter. Alternatively, they may be able to suggest other contacts to try if you were unsuccessful with them. This can be an excellent way of securing placements as it enables you to contact this second person with a personal reference from someone they know and trust, which instantly makes you a viable option for consideration.

By ringing up it also adds a human element to the letter and may make them more sympathetic to your request. Remember to introduce yourself and mention the letter and then check you are speaking to the correct person. Perhaps say that you are grateful for their consideration and was wondering whether they have come to a decision about whether you might be offered a placement. Most importantly, do not be too pushy, or give the impression that you are annoyed that they have not replied to you sooner.

Do not be disheartened if you are rejected from several places. Heléna was told by several hospitals that they only took students over 18 years of age or those from a particular 'linked' school. You will need to be persistent if you do not know a doctor that works in the hospital you are applying to.

If you are really having no luck then try getting in touch with your GP. He or she will have some contacts at the local hospital and may be able to help you. Most GPs will not allow their own patients to have work experience in their surgery because of patient confidentiality, but they may be able to give you a leg up somewhere else.

It is also not necessarily a bad thing to have some rejections for work experience. It may give you the opportunity to mention in your interview that you had to think laterally and show determination to get a place.

2.4 Evidence

In order to make the most of your work experience it can be useful to keep some important documents. Keep your rejection letters as evidence of the effort you have made. Once at your placement you could ask whether the doctor you are shadowing would be willing to write a short reference for you to take to your interview. They also provide an excellent source from which your teachers can quote when writing their section in your UCAS application.

It is a good idea to keep a little diary of what you did each day so that you can think about how you would expand on it for interview. This can be valuable if there is a large time gap between work experience and interview. You might want to write down the condition of a patient you met and what tests they had done, and perhaps an interesting feature of their treatment. However, remember to never write down the personal details of any patient you meet, including their name, address and hospital number as this goes against confidentiality.

Summary

So, the key points when it comes to work experience are:

- **Start as early as possible** - decide what placements you want and write or email early.
- **Variety** - this is the magic word. Aim to experience as much variety as you can in your placements.
- **Persistence** - expect a lot of "sorry but we are unable to help you" responses, but do not be put off as all it takes is the occasional success to make it all worthwhile.

Chapter 3

Choice of Medical School

This is one area of the application process where a lot of candidates and, in particular, concerned parents can fall into the trap of over thinking things. That's not to say that this is not a big decision, after all, you'll be spending the next five or six years of your life there, it's just that you need to be making the choice for the right reasons.

There still remains a widely held perception that there are certain schools which one 'should' go to because they are so highly regarded and their graduates are bound to get the plum jobs while graduates from the 'lesser' medical schools will be fighting for scraps on the job market. Let us dispel that myth right away. The fact is that all UK medical schools will provide a quality medical education and, more importantly, all of them will furnish you with that magic bit of paper on graduation that allows you to progress to working as a doctor within the UK. Furthermore, whilst ten or twenty years ago there could be a touch of the Old Boys Club affecting medical applications ("Ah yes, good old Jenkins played cricket for the Blues don'cherknow, scored a century against Oxford. Yes he'll make a fine orthopaedic surgeon, what. I say pass the port"), the current application process for Foundation jobs makes this type of favouritism impossible. It is a national, online application form with a series of short questions, each of which is scored by a separate panel. The only part that your medical school plays in your final score is that a small proportion of the marks are awarded according to your 'Quartile ranking' amongst the students in your year (in other words are you in the top 25% of exam results within your year at your medical school, from 25 to 50%, etc). This has actually led a few students at some of the traditionally more prestigious Universities to complain that they are being discriminated against due to the higher calibre of competition internally within their school! Yes, the grass **is** always greener on the other side.

3.1 Location, location, location

So, if there is no such thing as the medical school that you 'should' go to how do you choose where to apply? Well first of all, as mentioned above, it has to be somewhere that you would actually want to live since you'll be training there for a while. In fact, around half of graduates also choose to stay in the area of the country where they trained for their Foundation Years. All medical schools tend to be set in large towns or cities, but if you are the outdoorsy country type don't subject yourself to life in London just because of its reputation. On the other hand, if you can't contemplate life away from the Big Smoke with its bright lights, then you know which way you should be leaning in your application.

Now unless you happen to have moved around a lot during your formative years, the chances are you will not know all of the cities that house medical schools. So once you've narrowed your choices down a bit, you have got to go to a bunch of open days and, in addition to listening to all the stuff about the course, try to speak to a few current students about what life is like both inside and outside of the medical school community. And while you are at it why not poke your nose around town a bit to try and get a feel for the place - it might only be a snapshot but you can learn an awful lot in a day.

3.2 Course Structure

The second, equally important factor in your decision-making process has to be finding a course whose teaching methods will suit your learning style. There has been a revolution of sorts in medical teaching over the last ten years with universities and the General Medical Council recognising that stuffy, traditional lecture-based teaching does not necessarily equip students with the learning and problem solving skills that they will need as qualified doctors. There has therefore been a move towards so-called 'Problem Based Learning', or PBL, in which students are presented with a case that centres on the medical problems of a particular patient and are then sent away with a series of questions related to the patient's conditions and their management. After a period of self-directed study students then reconvene, generally in small groups, to discuss the issues raised by the case. At its best PBL can be amazingly effective as it gives a real feeling of relevance to the learning and, since the information is presented within a clinical context, it hopefully should be more memorable. It also starts students thinking through problems in the manner which they will need to as a doctor from an early stage.

Critics would, on the other hand, point out that presenting students with a problem and simply pointing them in the direction of the library or internet is a very different style of teaching to that which they will have been used to during their schooling up to this point and this can lead to some students feeling completely lost at sea in the vast mass of knowledge encompassed by medicine and the biomedical sciences. True cynics might say that this teaching style has been so fully embraced by universities because reducing the number of lectures cuts teaching costs, but this is quite unfair as the organisation required to teach in small groups and the provision of high quality resources for self-directed learning more than balance this out.

Most UK medical schools are using PBL to some degree in their courses, often in combination with other more traditional teaching methods, but there are a few that lean very heavily on the PBL style of teaching. It must be said that those that use it a lot tend to do it very well, but when choosing your medical school it is worth bearing in mind if that would suit your personality. Learning in this manner requires a good amount of self-motivation and focus to really get your teeth into each of the cases and get the most out of each of them, otherwise you'll run the risk of drifting along until a few weeks before your end of year exams when you realise just how much you have to do!

Going hand-in-hand with the rise of PBL is a move towards more integrated and systems-based teaching in many medical schools. What this boils down to is that, rather than the traditional way of learning anatomy in one block, then learning physiology quite separate to that, then perhaps the following year learning pathology and pharmacology, then later still actually seeing all of this in a clinical context, in an integrated course you would learn everything about a particular body system at the same time. So in one block of teaching you might, for example, take on the circulatory system. You would cover the anatomy of the heart and blood vessels, the physiology of how they work, pathological processes that affect them and drugs that act on them. Recently the GMC has also made recommendations for earlier clinical exposure in medical school courses so you may well also meet patients with circulatory problems at the same time. Medical schools have taken on this recommendation to wildly varying degrees. At a few you will meet your first living, breathing patient within a week or two of arriving at university, while at other places students are relatively sheltered from patient contact for the first couple of years – again a point of personal preference to bear in mind.

3.3 Academic Requirements

In general, most medical applicants are fairly confident types and this certainly is something that admission tutors look for (in certain branches of the medical profession it pays to have unshakable self-belief). My favourite preoperative quote from one of our cardiothoracic surgeons is the following: "Madam, there are only two people who can help you now. And God is not available." However, one of the skills of being a doctor is the ability to recognise your own limitations and this applies right at the start in the admissions process. If you look through the various medical school pages on the UCAS website you'll quickly see that some will tend to give considerably more demanding offers than others. For instance, places like Oxbridge value academic ability above almost everything else (including common sense at times) and have plenty of applicants who will get at least three A's at A level so that's what they will ask for and they will also look for a track record of academic success leading up to your application. What this means is that if, in your heart of hearts, you know that you are really going to struggle to reach those grades then you need to have other places that are less demanding in mind too. Now we don't want to sound discouraging and if your dream from as far back as you can remember is a place at Cambridge then by all means fire off an application to them - it's great to shoot for the stars. It is, however, worth making sure that some of your other choices are within your academic comfort zone. That way when you get to your Cambridge interview you'll hopefully be able to relax and swing for the fences, safe in the knowledge that you have a solid, realistic back-up plan.

3.4 Student Selected Components

Electives

All medical school courses recognise that each student has interests in particular fields which they may wish to pursue in more depth during their course. There are two main opportunities for doing this, the most exciting of which is the elective period. This is a period of 5 to 10 weeks usually taken in one of the last two years at medical school, where you can organise to work as a medical student in just about any department anywhere in the world as long as you can talk your way into it. Anything from high-powered neurosurgery in the United States to rural clinics in deepest darkest Africa is fair game, so no matter what you are in to it's great from a learning point of view. And, lets all be honest, it's also a fully endorsed excuse for a bit of a holiday too! Grants are available both within universities and from various national bodies to help fund electives so it's an opportunity to take advantage of.

Specialties

There will also be blocks of time in the medical course where students choose from a range of possible modules to be studied within their own university. It's worth putting this time to good use as you will often find that this is your last chance to try out various specialties and to demonstrate your commitment to them, as it's often not possible to get exactly the combination of jobs you want in your Foundation years. Then early on in FY2 you'll find yourself having to apply to more specialist training programmes, so it pays to have shopped around before that! Medical schools vary considerably in the length of time that they allow for electives and in the variety on offer in other optional modules. If these are things which appeal to you make sure you scrutinise the prospectus to find a school which will give you the flexibility that you desire.

3.5 Intercalated Degrees

The world of medical recruitment is becoming more competitive with each passing year, so having an extra degree on your CV certainly is going to make you more attractive to potential employers. Many medical schools offer the opportunity to add an extra year to the degree midway through the course to study one particular subject in detail, generally one of the biomedical sciences, and to do a research project. This will net you an extra degree such as a BSc in addition to your medical degree and will also show that you have had experience in research, both of which will score you extra points in job applications. Generally the chance to do an intercalated year is only offered to students reaching a certain academic standard in the first year or two of medical school, but it is worth noting that a few universities make all of their students go through this extra year. Oxford and Cambridge have, since the dawn of time, split their medical course into a three year preclinical degree and a three year clinical course with a degree awarded at the end of each. More recently, University College London and Imperial College London have extended their courses to six years as standard with a BSc being awarded. St. Andrews University is different in that it offers a 3 year preclinical degree in Medical Sciences after which you receive a BSc. It is then necessary to do a further 3 year clinical course at either another Scottish University or at Manchester. The University of Nottingham is noteworthy in that they run a 5 year course, but award a BMedSci degree at the end of year 3 without the need to do an extra year.

3.6   What if I did the wrong A-level subjects?

If, in some moment of inspiration you should happen to have chosen to be more creative in your choice of A levels than simply going for the sciences and you don't now have at least two out of Chemistry, Biology and Physics, fear not, there are still ways into med school! A fairly recent innovation has been the inception of 'Foundation' courses at a number of UK medical schools, which will take a limited number of students who have demonstrated high academic potential in non-science subjects and put them through a premedical year in which they cover enough of the basic science that they can then slot in with students starting the standard five year course a year later. Entry into the five year course is guaranteed provided the premedical year exams are passed. Due to the limited numbers of places these courses could be very competitive to get into, but at least it gives you a chance.

3.7 Other routes in

The University of Southampton offers a 'Widening Access' course which is designed to provide an opportunity for students whose backgrounds would normally make it difficult to get into medical school. Strict criteria ensure that places on this course are reserved for those in receipt of means-tested benefits/grants and those who would be in the first generation of their family to go through higher education. Students go through a premedical year covering topics in medical sciences and professional practice with extensive tutorial and pastoral support. Attainment of sufficient grades at the end of this year grants entry onto the standard five year course at Southampton. Other universities, such as King's College London, also positively select for applicants in deprived areas, aiming to level the playing field for those of you who may have had less opportunity to excel at school. These will require lower entrance grades than many other medical courses, but you must meet the 'social' criteria. Check with the individual universities or with UCAS for precise details of entry criteria.

St. George's Medical School (London) offer a Foundation for Medicine course for mature students (over the age of 21) who show evidence of post-GCSE study other than A-levels and degrees (e.g. GNVQ, Accountancy) and at least 3 years of progression on a professional career path. This is another course that covers basic biomedical sciences in one year and allows progression onto the standard five year course if a sufficient standard is reached.

3.8 Graduate Entry Courses

Since their inception almost a decade ago, shortened graduate entry medical courses have increased massively in number and in popularity with the GMC. In fact although our crystal ball is not always entirely accurate it appears that if, as is likely in a few years time, there are cuts in the number of places at medical schools nationally the graduate entry courses will probably suffer the least.

The government and the GMC like graduate students for a number of reasons. For starters they have had a chance to go and live a life, try other careers and, now that they are finally deciding to do medicine, they tend to be pretty certain in their decision. Since they have often given up other careers to go back to being a student it is very obvious exactly how much medical school is costing them and that certainly provides a healthy dose of motivation to work hard. Consequently, the majority of graduate entry courses feature a heavy dose of self directed and problem based learning, which can be a shock to those whose previous degrees have featured more traditional teaching methods.

Most of the graduate entry courses currently on offer (of which there are 16) follow a roughly similar structure. The first 12 to 18 months are a fairly frantic period where they attempt to cram all of the learning you would normally be doing in the first two to three years of the standard undergraduate course into a much shorter time. Add to this the fact that they all like to bring in clinical exposure as early as possible in the course and you can see why they are not for the faint hearted! After this initial period, the graduate students join in with the standard undergraduate course for the last two to three years of the course right through to finals. Swansea and Warwick are slightly unusual in that they only run graduate entry medical courses and do not take school leavers at all.

Because of the volume of information that needs to be picked up in the first year of most graduate courses, they tend to only be open to those with a degree in a related science subject on the basis that they are likely to have come across some of the material in their first degree. However, a few courses such as Keele and St. Georges are happy to take graduates in non-science subjects.

Although the work can be frenetic studying medicine on a graduate entry course, it adds a whole extra level of interest to the subject. Each person on the course will have a very different background and brings unique skills and perspectives to problems. For instance on Ross' course there were vets, accountants, neuroscientists, a healthcare economist ("the most cost efficient patient is a dead one" – helpful!) and others who had previously studied philosophy, psychology, politics and all sorts of sciences. Rarely was there a topic that at least one person didn't have an opinion on!

One noticeable benefit which comes with entry into medicine slightly later in life quickly becomes apparent on hospital wards. For some reason there is an assumption that more wrinkles equates to more experience and seniority so you are taken a lot more seriously from the start. Of course this can lead to the occasional sticky situation such as one of the first times Ross went down to the medical assessment unit in Oxford. No sooner had he arrived than he was grabbed by the ward sister with the words "Oh brilliant, so you must be the new gastroenterology registrar we called to do the urgent scope on the patient with haematemesis (i.e. vomiting up blood!)? Come on, he's just in here..."

Summary

Don't get too hung-up on 'which' medical school you 'should' apply to – you'll still become a doctor at the end of the day!

Important factors to consider include:
- Location
- Course structure – will it suit you?
- Academic requirements

There are a number of student-selected components to consider, such as 'Electives.'

There are a variety of routes into medicine, including Graduate Entry.

Profile: Dr Andy Holdstock
BSc (Hons) BMBS (Hons)

Andy is currently an F1 doctor in General Medicine at Nottingham City Hospital. He graduated from Nottingham University in 2010 with an Honours degree in Graduate Entry Medicine, having originally completed a BSc in Biochemistry at Bristol University in 2005.

Andy's Story

"When the time came for me to apply to University I was in a position whereby I had good A-levels, mostly science, but little idea of what I wanted to do with them. All I knew was that I wanted to go to University! Medicine was something I hadn't really considered. I went to study Biochemistry at Bristol University, mainly as I was interested and it seemed generic enough to keep my options open. By the end of my second year the question of a career was once more presenting itself and I had to consider what I might actually want to do once I graduated. I was interested in science, but the more practical, applicable side and I enjoyed working with people so a lab-based career wasn't really on the cards. At around this time, graduate entry medical courses had just been 'imported' to the UK from both the US (where it is all graduate entry) and Australia and had found acceptance amongst British universities and the UK medical profession. I hadn't considered medicine before this, but at the time it embodied a good mix of applicable science and people skills.

I opted to defer my application for a year and took a year out to work, both to save up for another course and also to get experience in a health care setting (an essential requirement for any medical course). After four months of working as a Health Care Assistant, shadowing doctors and speaking to current students I was certain that I wanted to apply for medicine.

The next question was 'where?' At the time my choice was rather limited as relatively few universities were offering four year fast-track courses. In addition two main types of courses were available: stand alone graduate entry courses (such as the one I accepted at Nottingham) and those with 'two in one' years, where, depending on your degree, you study part of the first year and part of the second in one year before sitting both sets of exams and progressing to the third year as part of the main undergraduate cohort. The entry requirements were fairly universal, a minimum of a 2.1 in a science based honours degree, although some courses will accept any degree and a 2.2 classification; these courses are usually 'stand alone' and will require you to sit an entrance exam such as the GAMSAT or UKCAT to demonstrate a certain level of ability.

The Nottingham GEM course required the GAMSAT which in addition to costing a fair bit is also pretty tough and competitive (in my year they interviewed the top 9%) so it is worth thinking hard to ensure that this is what you want to do. Graduate courses, like all medical courses are notoriously competitive, both due to their increasing popularity and the limited number of places (when I applied there were only 90 places at Nottingham and 7 applicants per place). Everyone I met when starting had worked hard to get there!

Graduate entry courses aren't for everyone. In the first 18 months the Nottingham course comprises of modules in pre-clinical medicine (taught via lectures and problem based learning seminars) and clinical experience in both classroom and in the community. At the end of this are written and practical exams before the GEM cohort join the undergraduate cohort for the two and a half clinical years. The pace is quick and there is a vast amount of material but the atmosphere and camaraderie is amazing, especially due to the small group work and practical teaching. Whilst the work was tough, I found it easier than some, having a good science background. The funding also differs. Whilst in the first year I had to pay my own fees (£3000 at Nottingham) but was eligible for a 'means-tested' student loan. For the remaining three years I was eligible for an NHS bursary; whilst this was 'means-tested' it meant that the NHS both paid my fees, travel costs to other sites and gave me a living allowance!

This was supplemented with a 'non means-tested' student loan - fortunate as there is little time for a part time job (which the course discouraged). Many of my course mates were older, having taken more than one year out, having had other careers or families, but the average age was under 30. There was still a vibrant social scene and much interaction with the undergraduate medical cohort. I certainly didn't miss out and had a LOT of fun.

At the time GEM courses were relatively new and finding their feet, but now, four years on, they are a common route in to medicine. Looking back I was neither ready nor willing to study medicine when I was fresh from school and in the current medical climate being slightly older, but more experienced, can only be beneficial for a career in medicine! I graduated from medicine at 26; if one were to do medicine at the age of 18, for five years, they'd graduate at 23. But to graduate with equivalent experience (a gap year, and a second degree via intercalation), something increasingly important with regards to foundation job applications, they'd qualify at 25!

So my advice is that if you are not 100% sure that medicine is for you right now, or you'd like to study something else in more detail first, think about graduate entry. There is more than one route into medicine and you're not disadvantaged for doing something else first... far from it!

So if I could go back and start my medical career differently, or more traditionally, would I? Hell no!"

"As it takes two to make a quarrel, so it takes two to make a disease, the microbe and its host."

Charles V. Chapin

Chapter 4

Making an Application to Medical School

Admissions tutors have perhaps one of the most important jobs in the entire medical profession. Why?

Because their decisions ultimately determine the future of the profession, as the people they choose to enter medical school are the same people who will go on to shape the health sector.

The assessment and decision they make about applicants - potentially you - is likely to be based on four fundamental questions:

1. Does the applicant have a real **motivation** to study medicine?

2. Is the applicant up to the **academic challenge** of the course?

3. Is the candidate **suitable to study medicine** (as guided by the 'fitness to practice' principles of the General Medical Council)?

4. Is the applicant **suited to the *particular* medical school** in question?

We will discuss these four areas in turn and give some top tips on how you can prove to the admissions tutors that you are a good candidate with regard to each section. You may find it useful to flick to other parts of the book that discuss some topics in more detail. We will then mention some other things that the tutors are likely to have in the back of their minds.

4.1 Motivation to study Medicine

One of the main things admissions tutors like to see is a true desire to study medicine. They really lap it up. It should not be hard to show if you are serious about a career in medicine and a little bit of research (such as reading this book) can certainly help the cause! Heléna was told by an admissions tutor that what excites him in an applicant is a "thirst for knowledge". You need to portray this from your personal statement and right through into interview. You should show your motivation to study medicine in your evidence of work experience and research into the vocation. Do you know what the course and career entail? Tutors want to see you have aspiration above and beyond just becoming a medical student. What do you aspire to in the future? Chapters 'Why Medicine' and 'Work Experience' focus on this. It looks great if you have a topic that you are interested in and have done some reading around the subject. At interview motivation also comes across in your demeanour. Do you look enthused to be in the interview? How do you react to not knowing the answer to a question, or maybe getting it wrong? Are you despondent or do you have another shot? This type of approach will be further covered in the 'Interview' chapter.

4.2 Academics: Grades and Admissions Exams

Medicine is one of the most academically challenging courses around. It is not in the interests of medical schools or, in fact, you to undertake a course that is too demanding for your academic abilities. Of course there are objective ways we measure academic achievement, but this does not always tally with potential to achieve at medical school. So, you can understand why the grade requirements and tests exist to filter applicants to medical school, but admissions tutors and universities as a whole are usually sensitive to detecting potential.

There are several paths you may navigate to study medicine. These include the 'standard' A-level approach, the Highers route in Scotland, international exams such as the International Baccalaureate, and finally graduate entry. There are other options that you can research on the UCAS website if you think these will not suit you. If you think you may not have the necessary grades or correct subjects then have a read of the 'Foundation Degree' section later in this chapter. The bulk of this section will relate to the A-level system. If you are one of the increasing numbers of people who are sitting, or have sat, the International Baccalaureate or are studying Highers and Advanced Highers then we have included a brief overview of what to expect, although we also advise that you check out the UCAS website for specific requirements.

Scottish Highers

A typical offer under the Scottish system is to ask for five Highers including Chemistry and then two of Biology, Maths and Physics. English Language is sometimes needed as part of this combination. Most universities also want Chemistry and another subject should be taken to Advanced Higher, although some universities require three. Grades tend to be set at straight As or a mixture of As and Bs. It may be acceptable to have one of the sciences at Intermediate level if not studied at Higher level but check with individual universities. Also bear in mind that many universities stipulate that the grades must be achieved at the first sitting.

International Baccalaureate (IB)

There are many medical students who have sat the International Baccalaureate, both abroad and in the UK. Again, different Medical Schools have slightly varying tariffs. Generally, you will need to have taken Chemistry and at least a second or sometimes third Science or Maths to Higher level. There will also be a tariff set for Subsidiary level, and an overall score set, usually between 34 and 39, depending on the university.

If you aim to follow the 'standard' entry pathway then people who tell you grades are not important at this stage are misleading you. Although A-level grades may not be available to the tutors, they will have your GCSEs and possibly AS results to hand. Medical schools will set a minimum standard for GCSE grades, particularly in science, maths and English at least. If you do not have these then you are unlikely to make it past the first screening process. Whilst medical schools often officially say they require 5 grades at A or B plus a 'good' grade in English, in fact, the vast majority of candidates have better grades than this. Many have straight As and A*s. Although this is not essential It is important to emphasise how important these GCSE grades are and it is likely that many of you have already taken them. However, if you are yet to take them here are some tips:

- You will need to take at least eight or so subjects, with many medical schools requiring more. You will need to have taken chemistry, either as part of a combined, or single science programme.

- Try to also have some breadth in your choices to show that you come with a range of disciplines and knowledge. Look on the UCAS website and the medical schools' own websites for specific GCSE requirements for each university.

A-level requirements vary between universities, but most will require at least As and Bs. They may also require a particular grade for AS level. As so many applicants have very good grades some medical schools now also look at your unit grade marks if they are available. Your AS levels and predicted A-levels should be at least close to the minimum required by the university. If they are not then your referee should explain why in their section of the UCAS form, giving details of any extenuating circumstances.

Needless to say that your AS levels are very important. Not only do they count for half of your GCE grade, they also give admissions tutors a flavour of how you are coping at this stage. Poor AS grades may be picked up at interview, or even affect whether you are called at all. So remember, even though you may have the opportunity to re-take these exams, they are important. One tip that some candidates take if they have flunked their AS levels, but with decent GCSEs, is to not certificate these exams and let their referee report be testament to their current programme. Some schools do this as standard, others think it is a bad idea and will not allow you to.

4.3   Which subjects should you study?

Be aware from as early as possible that some medical schools do not accept subjects such as General Studies as an AS-level or A-level. They almost always require chemistry, and some require biology to an AS or A2 level. The days of requiring three or more sciences at A-level are diminishing, but many medics do find biology at A-level to be useful when studying for the medical degree. Some universities may actually like you to have a different subject at A-level so long as you are sensible in your choice. Heléna studied English literature at A-level, along with biology and chemistry, and maths to AS, and was accepted to all the medical schools she applied to. This was a difficult decision for her to make as she was worried about dropping maths, but having checked the individual A-level requirements she was not put off. In the end it caught the attention of some admissions tutors and she was able to talk passionately about a subject she really enjoyed. This may work to your advantage and give you a fresh perspective to other applicants. So do not necessarily be put off studying a non-science subject if you know your chosen medical schools do not require a full house of purely science subjects.

4.4 How many subjects should you study?

Another question that is regularly asked is whether applicants are better off studying four or more subjects to get more A-levels, or to drop some to focus their energy and effort on fewer and thus increase their chances of getting higher grades. This is a very personal decision and depends on lots of factors. Even the top medical schools only actually require three A-levels (plus your dropped AS). You should not stretch yourself too thinly and risk missing the grade requirements. Better to get two As and a B than five Bs and miss out on your conditional offer of AAB.

The other thing to remember is that by studying additional subjects you may make life more difficult for yourself by attracting a conditional offer for all of your subjects. For example, at the time of print, Imperial (London) requires AAA for A-level with a grade B at AS, but if four subjects are taken then this increases to a requirement of AAAC plus B at AS.

Consider saving and prioritising some of your time for work experience and extra curricular activities, which are also essential for your application. There is probably more scope in this area to improve your chances of success than by adding another subject. However, if you are certain that you can handle the work and would actually like to study more subjects then go for it.

If you are at all unsure about your subject choices or grades then it is always best to check the most up-to-date information for specific medical schools on the UCAS website.

4.5 Admission Tests: UKCAT, BMAT & GAMSAT

There are now only a fraction of medical schools that do not require applicants to sit a test. They have become necessary to distinguish between the large number of candidates with good grades. The two main tests for school leavers are the UKCAT and the BMAT, and each work slightly differently. If you are applying to medical schools that require different tests, you will have to take both. Some people would advise that you try to 'spread your risk' between the exams. This means that if you have a bad day and get an unexpectedly low mark, you have another chance to sit another exam, or be considered by a medical school that does not have an admissions test. This may be a good idea for some candidates, but try not to be put off somewhere you really love for this reason.

The tests are not meant to be coached or crammed, but in reality it is in your best interests to at least familiarise yourself with the format of the paper and the type of questions that will be asked before you walk into the door.

Another essential piece of advice is to organise your registration and payment well in advance. You can usually do this through your college, but there are other test centres all around the country. UKCAT registration begins in May, and BMAT in September. Do not leave it until the last minute and get in a panic!

The UKCAT, at the time of print, costs £60 if taken before September, and £75 if sat between September and 9th October. It costs £95 if taken outside the EU. The BMAT, at the time of print, costs £32.10 and everyone takes the test on the same day, usually in early November. It costs £55.90 at the time of print for international students. You will be entitled to a bursary if you receive EMA of £30, but if you are worried about the cost then speak to your school about possible assistance.

Do not worry too much about taking these tests, and certainly do not let them put you off applying for medicine. Everyone is in the same boat, and a poor score does not necessarily mean your application will be unsuccessful.

UKCAT

The UKCAT is now required by over 20 medical schools (correct at time of publication):

University/ Medical School	UCAS Code
University of Aberdeen	A100
Brighton & Sussex Medical School	A100
Barts & The London School of Medicine & Dentistry	A100, A101, A200, A201
Cardiff University	A100, A104, A200, A204
University of Dundee	A100, A104, A200
University of Durham	A100
University of East Anglia	A100, A104
University of Edinburgh	A100
University of Glasgow	A100, A200
Hull York Medical School	A100
Keele University	A100, A104
King's College London	A100, A101, A102,

	A103, A202, A203, A205
Imperial College London Graduate Entry	A101
University of Leeds	A100
University of Leicester	A100, A101
University of Manchester	A104, A106, A204, A206
University of Newcastle	A100, A101, A206
University of Nottingham	A100
University of Oxford Graduate Entry	A101
Peninsula College of Medicine & Dentistry	A100
Queen's University Belfast	A100, A200
University of Sheffield	A100, A104, A200
University of Southampton	A100, A101, A102
University of St Andrews	A100, B900
St George's, University of London	A100
Warwick University Graduate Entry	A101

It takes two hours to complete and takes the form of multiple-choice questions on a computer.

It consists of five subsets:

1. Verbal reasoning

2. Quantitative reasoning

3. Abstract reasoning

4. Decision analysis

5. Non-cognitive analysis

They are timed separately. The UKCAT, unlike the BMAT, does not aim to test scientific knowledge but rather an applicant's aptitude. It also takes into account some of your personal characteristics that medical schools wish students to have, such as an ability to empathise with others. For more information visit the UKCAT website at:

www.ukcat.ac.uk

BMAT

The BMAT is a test required by four medical schools: Cambridge, Oxford, Imperial College London and UCL (University College London). It takes two hours to complete and has three sections.

Unlike the UKCAT, it does require some scientific knowledge up to GCSE standard in biology, physics, chemistry and maths. You may find it useful to look over some GCSE revision guides for these subjects if you dropped them after GCSE.

The first section tests "aptitude and skills" which is jargon for whether you can analyse data and make inferences to solve problems.

The second section is a multiple choice test covering "scientific knowledge and applications" which is the part that you will need your science and maths for. Unfortunately you are not allowed a calculator so make sure you know your times tables!

The third section is a "writing task" where you get to choose from a list of three essay questions. Your answers will need to be short and concise as there is likely to be a limited space to in which to write.

Heléna took the BMAT as a bright young sixth-former. She arranged it through her school and did not do much extra work for it. On the day, timing was very important. Make sure you take a watch and if you cannot answer a question in time then make an educated guess and move on. Best to risk getting that question wrong than not finish the paper. For more information check out the website at:

www.admissionstests.cambridgeassessment.org.uk

Graduate Tests

For those graduates amongst you, there are some additional tests you should be aware of. You may have to take the GAMSAT (Graduate Medical School Admissions Test) or just the usual UKCAT or BMAT.

At the time of print, the GAMSAT is required by five medical schools:

1. St George's, University of London

2. The University of Nottingham at Derby

3. The University of Wales in Swansea

4. Keele University and

5. The 5-year degree at The Peninsula Medical School

It is especially important if applying to Peninsula Medical School (Universities of Exeter & Plymouth) as the admissions tutors here use it as the only measure of your academic performance and do not consider your A-levels or degree grades. It consists of three papers with reasoning in humanities and social sciences as well as biological and physical sciences, with an additional written communication section.

It is fairly unavoidable and those who did not study a science for their degree will find the test difficult, but it is not impossible to do well. The main drawback of this test is it costs a whopping £192 (correct at the time of print). You must register by late August and there are only five test centres in the UK, plus one in Australia for international applicants.

For more information on the GAMSAT check out ***www.gamsatuk.org***

4.6   Fitness to Practice

Doctors and medical students come into contact with some very vulnerable people. The General Medical Council regulates doctors to ensure the safety of the public. Medical Schools have a responsibility to not admit those people who they judge may pose a threat to society. They also monitor students throughout their studies. This assessment takes a number of forms. As part of your UCAS form application you will have to declare whether you have any criminal convictions or cautions. Everyone makes mistakes, and having one does not automatically equal rejection. However, lying about a conviction would result in rejection. You will have to have a criminal records check anyway so do not hide anything. On a similar note, being shown to act dishonestly or cheating in exams would also ring alarm bells. You need to show that you are the sort of person that people could trust with their lives. You must be aware in your personal statement and interview that extreme and dangerous beliefs will be held against you.

51

For example, a candidate that thinks all people with HIV should be shot will not be accepted to become a doctor. Thank goodness! So, basically the vast majority of you will be fine, but declare any trouble you have gotten into and do not apply for medicine if you have views that do not tally to those accepted by the medical community. For more information check out the GMC website and their document on 'Tomorrow's Doctors' at *www.gmc-uk.org*

4.7 Suitability to the particular Medical School

As you have hopefully realised by now, all medical schools are subtly, if not vastly different. They teach the curriculum in different ways and they test you in different ways. They put differing levels of importance on academic achievement or on interpersonal development. Medical schools can be based in big cities or smaller towns. They are allied to their own universities, which have their own personalities. Admissions tutors will probably try to tease out whether you actually want to go there, or whether their university is at the bottom of your list. They are not allowed to ask directly though. How do they know this then? Well, they may ask you about how you like to learn. If you are applying to a problem-based learning centre then at least mention it! If you are applying to Oxbridge then mention the tutorial system. Heléna was asked in one of her interviews whether she knew which local hospitals she would be based at. This was probably to test whether she had read the prospectus and had thought about actually coming to that university. Have a think in advance why you have chosen that university and always be familiar with the prospectus! Maybe it is great for the sport you like playing, or maybe you like to be beside the sea. Try to have an academically based answer as well, even if this is not actually at the top of your list of reasons for applying there. Admissions tutors, like most of us, enjoy being flattered, so tell them how great you think their medical school is and hopefully they will tick the box on your application.

4.8   What else do Admissions Tutors look for?

As well as looking at each candidate's merits as an individual, admissions tutors, in a more general sense, will try to ensure that the people they choose to become tomorrow's doctors and serve the community are representative of it. In layman's terms this means they want a variety of characters from a variety of backgrounds. The reason for this makes sense: doctors work to solve problems and need the knowledge and experience to be able to understand the problems that different sectors of society face. What this boils down to is that you should never be put off applying for medicine because you think you are not the right 'type'. Traditionally, doctors were white, middle class men but nowadays things are different. Many people believe that the intake to medical school is now broadly representative of society in terms of gender and ethnicity but lacking in terms of socio-economic breadth.

The Department of Health is now committed to tackling the under-representation of poorer groups and there are several projects that have been set up to improve access to medical school from people who might not usually apply. If you think you might be in this group, then you may be able to take advantage of local 'widening participation' schemes or the 'gifted and talented' programme in schools.

Contact your careers advisor or a teacher for more information on how you can utilise these opportunities.

Summary

Think about whether you are personally and academically suitable to study medicine, as well as motivated to do it. Make sure you have sat suitable subjects and achieved high enough grades to make an application. Be aware of, and prepare for admissions tests in advance. This involves identifying which universities want what. Remember there is more to your application than academic results, but you cannot do without them!

Chapter 5
UCAS Form

The UCAS form is an essential gatekeeper to the interview process and an offer of a place at medical school. Everyone must complete one and it is imperative that you get this part of the process right. Each medical school will look at this form in addition to entry exams to decide whether they want to meet you face-to-face. In some rare cases universities, such as Southampton and Edinburgh, do not interview and use the UCAS form and grades as their sole method of selection.

One of the most important things is to not miss the deadline! It may sound ridiculously obvious but you would be amazed at how many applicants miss out in this way. So check this nice and early. Last year the deadline for submitting UCAS applications for medicine was 15th October. This is earlier than most other UCAS deadlines so you will need to be more on the ball than those students applying to other courses. Remember not to leave the completion of the form too late; you will need time to alter and refine the application before you hit the final submit button. Some people find it useful to set a schedule of when they aim to have written a first draft and have it checked, so that things are not rushed at the end. The UCAS website (*www.ucas.ac.uk*) is an excellent resource to check deadlines and also to submit the form itself. You can use the website to track your application and check its progress. If you do not have access to the internet, either at home or school, then you will need to contact UCAS to discuss how you can submit your application.

The UCAS form has seven sections to complete:

1. Personal details

2. Additional information (UK applicants only)

3. Choices of course

4. Education

5. Employment

6. Personal statement

7. Reference

Once you have completed sections 1-6 and are happy with what you have included and would not wish to further change it, you send the application and the fee to the person who is writing your reference. At the time of print, submitting a UCAS application costs £19, and £9 if you are only making one choice on your form. There are bursaries available for those who are in financial difficulty. The person that is writing your reference will then complete the last section and send off the entire application to UCAS. It is obviously advisable that the person who writes the reference has read your application and does not write anything that will contradict what you have written in your application. Universities do read this section and a good or damaging reference can certainly sway their decision in offering an interview, or even a place. Referees typically include your predicted grades and why you are suitable to study medicine in their section. Do not expect them to write complementary things if they are not a great fan of yours! Try to find out who will be writing your reference and at least make sure they know who you are. They may also comment on your performance in a particular subject or on how you have contributed to the school community in a particular way. For some students who have, or are expecting to have difficulties that will affect academic performance, the reference section offers a platform for explaining these special circumstances. This should only be done with your permission, but may improve your chances if you miss your grades because of extenuating factors. It is worth remembering that you are legally entitled to see your referee report under the Data Protection Act. The reference is meant to paint you in a good light so if you have had a run in with the teacher writing it, try and get into their good books well in advance. It may seem creepy, but we call it smart career engineering!

5.1 Course Code

Another vitally important and seemingly obvious thing to point out is to make sure that you have put the correct course code on your application. There are several medically-related courses studied at university that will not give you a medical degree to be a doctor. Do not be one of the silly people who apply for biomedical sciences, having mistaken it for medicine! The standard entry code is A100, the graduate entry is A101 and the foundation entry A104.

Once you have researched the courses and universities you would like to apply for, have read prospectuses and been to open days, you are ready to start filing out the form.

5.2 Common Application Questions

There are a few questions that are frequently asked by students and we have tried to answer these below:

1. How many courses can I include in my application?

The answer is as many as you like. You are restricted to a maximum of four medical school choices, and a total number of five choices. Many people fill up their four medical spots and then use a related degree such as biomedical sciences or veterinary science as a back up. Other

58

people may feel that if they missed out on medicine they would rather do something different, like English. There are two main things to bear in mind if this relates to you. First, the tutors from each of your choices will read your personal statement. An English tutor may be quite confused as to why you are applying for English if your first line is "I have always been fascinated by the working of the human body." Similarly, medical admissions tutors may be a little questioning of your commitment to their course if you mention your love of Shakespearean sonnets. Fortunately, tutors cannot see the actual choices you have made unless you have made two applications to the same university. For example, Bristol medical school could not tell that you have applied for veterinary at Cambridge, but could see if you applied for veterinary at Bristol. You will likely be shot down in flames for this at interview, so steer clear! To summarise, you will have to base your decision on a balance between your desire for an insurance choice (and whether you tailor some of your personal statement towards this) and running the risk of having your commitment to medicine being called into question.

2.   Which course should I choose as an insurance?

As alluded to in the previous answer, the course you decide to use as your insurance is a personal decision. Despite what people tell you, there is no right answer. The best advice we can give is that if you think that you failed in your attempt to be a doctor, you would rather do something completely different then you may need to question whether medicine is actually right for you. However, having said that, Heléna planned to study English literature if she failed to gain a spot at medical school, yet she is completely committed to becoming a doctor. Lots of people feel they would prefer to go and do a related degree such as biology or biomedical science, which some people then use to enter medicine as a graduate student. This shows real determination and obviously puts you at an advantage when you eventually do study medicine as you will be used to tackling scientific concepts and conducting research.

3. Could I transfer from another course?

Although not unheard of this is extremely unlikely. You would need to be very up-front with the admissions tutor when you start your course and you may need to follow the medical admissions system with the next cohort of applicants. Basically do not bank on being able to take this route into medicine.

4. Should I take a Gap Year?

Gap years are becoming increasingly popular for medical applicants. They can be a fantastic opportunity to travel the world or perhaps earn some cash before you head off to university. The time is a blank canvas for you to do anything you decide, and is likely to leave you more confident and mature. Gap years can act as a nice break before the marathon of medical school, so long as you are sure you will make the starting line next year! Do bear in mind that you will obviously qualify and start earning your first salary a year later. Medical schools are unlikely to mind you deferring for a year, so long as you tick the box on the application. In fact, you may be quizzed about your plans at interview and be given the golden opportunity to explain how you plan to experience things that will certainly make you a better doctor.

Obviously, if you plan to sit on the sofa playing computer games for a year, this may not help your cause, so you should have a few plans to talk about at interview. If you are interested in travelling later in your medical career, as a qualified doctor, there are lots of opportunities between various levels to take a year out, so a year out before university is not the only chance for travel that you will have.

5. I have missed the grades for my first choice. What should I do?

Do not panic! Get on the phone as soon as possible to the admissions tutor. This may lead to you being pleasantly surprised to learn that you impressed so much at interview that they will relax the requirements. They may be able to offer you some useful advice if this is not the case, which may help improve your chances of success if you decide to reapply the following year. Alternatively, you may have an insurance choice that had a lower grade offer and who you can accept a place with.

5.3 The Personal Statement

This is probably the most important document you will write in your application to study medicine. You are essentially trying to catch the eye of the admissions tutor and convince them to invite you for the coveted interview. You have limited space in which to write so you need to be good at putting the essential information in a succinct and effective manner. Your personal statement is likely to be in a pile of hundreds of others so you need to make sure your statement finds itself safely into the 'interview' pile. It needs to have a certain amount of essential information in it, which we will cover in this chapter. It should also be organised, logical and easy to read, being set out in clear paragraphs, perhaps with subheadings. Lots of people find writing this document daunting, but don't worry. With our help you should be well on the way to putting a smile on the admissions tutor's face.

An important thing to remember when writing your personal statement is that it is *your* personal statement. We can give you tips on how to strengthen it but ultimately it will be made up of your ideas and experiences. Do not bother plagiarising. You are likely to be caught out and it will ruin your chances of becoming a medic. Everyone has their own style of writing and you should write something that fits in with how you will present yourself at interview. Make sure you have checked spelling and grammar thoroughly. Bear in mind that the medical personal statement is quite different from those for other subjects. You may not have a careers advisor or teacher that is familiar with what is required. If this is the case it may be a good idea to get in touch with a medical student or doctor who can have a read through what you have written before it is sent off. Similarly, a teacher or other trusted adult will be able to offer useful feedback. If you really can't find someone you trust to read and give feedback on your statement then there are a number of services available which offer personal statement review and analysis. This obviously does come at a price though.

As a general guide to how you structure your statement, you should include:

1. Why you want to be a doctor

2. Outline your work experience

3. Evidence of working with people

4. Interests and Hobbies (extra curricular achievements)

We will outline each section in turn to give you an idea of what to include. One rule you should aim to follow is whenever you make a statement about something you have been interested in or experienced, aim to relate this back to how it applies to medicine. This will hopefully make things relevant to your application. It is also important to bear in mind at this stage that admissions tutors will often use the personal statement as a skeleton for the interview, so be prepared to expand on, and justify what you have written face to face.

1. Why you want to be a doctor

This is an obvious question you need to answer early on in the personal statement. It has been covered in the 'Why Medicine' chapter and elsewhere in the book. You should try to give a semi-unique answer, although it is difficult to avoid giving a clichéd response. Try not to say things like, "I have always wanted to be a doctor," as it does not really tell the admissions tutor anything. You might prefer to say, "For many years I have had a desire to apply scientific knowledge to treat disease in the community," as it has a bit more meat on the bone, despite saying roughly the same thing. You may have a particularly interesting experience that triggered a desire to study medicine such as using your first aid skills to help save a life. This is a great way of conveying the idea and would make you stand out from the crowd. Obviously, if you do not have such a story then do not make it up as you could land yourself in trouble at interview! In this section of the statement it may be appropriate to give an indication of the fact that you understand the true challenge of being a doctor. This should be a theme that pops up throughout the statement, and is a major criterion on which you are likely to be judged.

2. Outline your Work Experience

Again, check out the 'Work Experience' chapter for details on what sort of work experience you should aim to do and what to get out of it. There is a really good chance that work experience will be brought up at interview so you should prepare yourself well. Remember, the interviewer will be able to tell a liar a mile off. You need to have actually done what you say you have done, and then do some reading around it so you can expand on it at interview. For example, Heléna gave an example of a time on her work experience when a CT scan of a patient with cystic fibrosis was being reviewed. She wrote about the fact that the pancreas showed pathology but the lungs were healthy because of a transplant. She was indeed asked about this case at two interviews. She read up about the gene defect present in cystic fibrosis, how this leads to changes in transport across cells and how it manifests as disease throughout the body. Do not fear; you do not need to know the full complexities of what you have chosen to research. However, from this sort of approach, tutors will see that you engaged in your work experience and were interested and organised enough to learn more about something independently. If you can get the message across that you were not just doing work experience to tick the boxes (which you weren't, right?) but that you were using it to inform your decision about studying medicine then you are on to a winner.

3. Evidence of working with people

As discussed in the 'Work Experience' chapter, you should be able to show that you have done some voluntary or community work. This should display that you are the sort of caring person that is suitable to study medicine and that you appreciate this is involved in the profession. It should ideally be over a lengthy period, to show that you have been committed enough to turn up and follow the task through. Maybe you have worked in a hospital serving up meals in the school holidays, or perhaps set up a football team for young people. You need to be able to relate this back to why it will make you a good doctor. For instance, it may be a good idea to make a statement about your experience, and how you expect it to help you as a doctor. An example of this may be ' I found my time coaching the children's football team to strengthen my perseverance, as it took up many of my weekends, but the reward in helping the team strengthen and grow was well worth it. I realise that medicine will also be a tough challenge, but I feel it will be justified by the satisfaction knowing I am helping those truly in need.'

There is also scope to talk about your experience working in a medical team. Did you have experience working with a nurse or in reception whilst on work experience? Were you able to work with different people effectively, despite them having different aspirations to yours? You may have been surprised by a 'them and us' culture between doctors and nurses at your work experience that you could mention in your statement. These examples would show that you are able to put yourself in someone else's shoes and treat others how you would like to be treated, the crux of modern medicine, some would argue. There is a plethora of other examples of effective teamwork you could include, and you may want to slot it into a different section, such as your hobbies, if more relevant.

4. Interests and Hobbies

The selectors will want to get a sense of who you are as a character. As alluded to throughout the book, lots of different characters choose to study medicine and do very well. Some of you will be naturally well rounded individuals with tonnes of hobbies and achievements that you could reel off. Remember the golden rule which is to make it relevant to studying medicine and being a doctor! For those of you who are not out playing rugby every evening or starring in the school production, you should be able to write about something which you do in your spare time and talk about how it is relevant and shows you can interact with people and work in a team. This may be the area of the statement you find most challenging as everyone is different. You could join an orchestra or team, or even get a part-time job to show you have great people skills. For others, of course, this section will more or less write itself. A frightening number of you will be prefects or head boy/girl, captain a sports team or have another exciting activity to talk about. You are likely to be asked about this at interview so have some stories about how it relates to medicine. Maybe you had to work in a team with someone you disagreed with? How did you manage it? How might that scenario arise in your career and how would your experience help?

Other Considerations

For those of you who are particularly keen on a specific type of course (eg Problem-Based Learning) you may also like to add in a section that strengthens your case. Obviously, you should be wary of this is if you are applying to a broad range of schools. Try not to flatter one university at the expense of another. However, if you are applying to medical schools that all offer an intercalated degree or offer a research-focused approach it would be helpful to include a section on some of your research interests and experiences. For example, Heléna arranged some experience in a cancer research laboratory, and also wrote about how this applied to medical practice. She was asked about this at interview which gave her the chance to expand on some extra reading she had done, and thus impress the interview panel. Alternatively, if you are applying to courses that offer newer problem-based approaches, you may feel it appropriate to write about why you feel this would suit you, and any experience you have had that informs this decision. For example, is there a particular project that you have worked on which highlighted your excellent ability to work in a small team to tackle a problem?

Check, check and check again!

Once you have written the statement make sure you check it and recheck it. Then check it again. Get people to read it and ask for feedback. Remember our advice is only a guide and you may want to say things that are not covered here. As a mature student you may have a lot more to add in which case you should contact the admissions tutor and request to send a CV with your UCAS reference on it. Your referee's report can also add to what you have written in your statement. Hopefully it will highlight your academic ability and also testify to your contribution to life at school or within the community.

5.4   What happens after the application has been sent?

Your tutor will complete your application by adding their reference. Once UCAS has received the application, they will send a receipt called a 'Welcome Letter' to you, your school or college. This should happen within 14 days. This receipt has some important information that you should check, such as the choice of course and universities. Make sure you have given your correct personal details, as you will receive information about your application through the post and via your UCAS account online. If anything is wrong, contact UCAS customer services to rectify it.

Once you have received the 'Welcome Letter' you will be able to 'track' your application online. Most people now choose this method to manage their application and you will have to make special arrangements if you do not have access to the internet. You can amend your details here, see the status of your application and even make your decision to accept or reject an offer online. You may also receive this information by post, and universities also often contact you directly to tell you they are considering your application, or to invite you for interview. Be aware that your application will be processed over a period of weeks to months, so be on your toes and check your UCAS account and your post! Similarly, do not be disheartened if you do not hear anything for a few months - this waiting game is very common and does not mean you will not get a place. If you are unsure about any part of this process, contact your careers advisor or UCAS directly.

Summary

Research which universities you would like to apply to, and be aware of their requirements.

Make sure you apply for the correct course.

Try to make your personal statement individual to you, but include basic information on your motivation to study medicine, your work experience, community work and any special interests you may have.

Make sure you track your application with UCAS.

Example Personal Statement

Hélena Gresty

Below is a copy of Heléna's very own personal statement she submitted as a fresh-faced sixth-former. Remember that every one is different (that, in fact, is the point!) and that your statement does not have to follow this line. It should, however give you an example of the basics, and give you a flavour of content and style that was successful in securing four interviews.

Hélena's Personal Statement

"I am passionate about studying medicine because of the academic, physical and emotional challenges involved and the great rewards it reaps. I am confident Medicine is my vocation as I enjoy being active in the community whilst driving to reach my own goals.

Much of my inspiration came from a two-week work experience placement at Northwick Park Hospital in the radiology department. I particularly enjoyed the lateral thinking required when reviewing radiographs. In one particular HO (House Officer) training session, the challenge was to analyse a CT scan showing fatty replacement and cysts in the pancreas, but healthy lungs. The consultant pointed out a crack in the sternum indicating previous chest surgery and the HO were able to ascertain that the patient suffered from Cystic Fibrosis but had received a lung transplant. This experience also built upon my MEDSIM course in Nottingham, where I learnt to take basic histories and make a diagnosis. I enjoyed seeing real people being treated with compassion and professionalism.

Working with elderly people in my local Sheltered Housing Project for two years has reminded me of the caring approach required in the medical profession. The time I spent there has helped me sympathise with the extremes of the human condition and I have come to realise the value of palliative care in the community, as well as cures.

My interest in medical research has been reinforced by spending two weeks in the labs of the Institute of Cancer Research in July and also earlier at the Royal Society of Science in 2002. On a more academic level, I have been interested in following the way in which the mapping of the human genome has driven research onwards. I look forward to the possible implications this research will have in oncological treatment when I am a doctor and am excited at the prospect of joining an evolving profession. I also feel the opportunity to study a BSc will prepare me for the demanding journey in medicine ahead.

I enjoy being both a leader and a team player, working with others and learning new things. I feel that my election as Head Girl this year shows that I am a good role model and I enjoy bridging the gap between students and teachers and the communication this involves. Gaining my Bronze and Silver Duke of Edinburgh and looking forward to being presented with my Gold has introduced me to new friends and exciting experiences. I have recently completed a four-day canoeing expedition down the river Severn. I also play hockey for my school and have represented Eastcote at U18 level. I have been able to contribute to my school by setting up our first ever student-run, professionally printed newspaper, THREE:20, as its editor. I also enjoy organising the mentoring system at my school as I am able to pass on my own experiences, advice and support to others and channel my energy into something positive. My paid work behind the bar at my local pub and teaching the piano to an eight-year-old has allowed me to use my talents to help others and I was delighted when my student passed her grade 2 exam this year! I play the piano to grade 8 myself, however the pleasure for me is in the private expression which it affords.

Although I am very aware of the combination of academic and personal demands medicine make, I feel most certain that becoming a doctor would be a huge privilege that I would embrace."

Profile: Simon Tyler
MBChB

Simon graduated from Birmingham Medical School in 2004 after completing the undergraduate medical degree.

Simon's Story

"Thinking back, I struggle to remember when I first decided that I wanted to become a doctor. I do know that for as long as I can remember this is what I wanted to do with my life. I was attracted by the mixture of the practical and the intellectual sides of medicine and also by the strong desire not to work in an office.

Out of the four medical schools that I applied to I was only interviewed by one of them (luckily my top choice) and at the time this worried me. However, after talking to my colleagues I have found out that this is by far the norm so don't worry if you don't get as many offers as you expected.

During my fourth year I sat on the interview panel for a day and we were given a series of characteristics to look for in prospective medical students. The high academic qualifications are pretty much a given nowadays so the panel are looking for proof that you have interests and hobbies beyond the scope of medicine. I know the phrase 'well rounded individual' is a little overused nowadays but it is still an important feature of any future medical student. Of course it is very important that you at least have some rudimentary communication skills and that you show some interest in medicine, so doing some work

72

experience and reading around the subject a little before your interview are vital.

The way my course, and I believe most medical courses, was structured was two years of academia followed by three years of clinical experience. By the end of my second year I was struggling somewhat to see the relevance of what we were learning and felt that I still hadn't the first clue about curing sick people. I stuck with the course however and when third year started and we were finally out in hospitals getting our hands on real people it all seemed worth it.

There is a myriad of opportunities to get involved with extra curricular activities at medical school, from sports to charity. I found myself signing up for things as diverse as Thai boxing and teaching sex education to secondary school children and I would advise that you get involved. There's the obvious advantage that they look good on your CV and give you things to talk about on your foundation year applications but I think it is also important to have a life outside medicine, just to let off a bit of steam every now and then.

It is also possible to take a year or more out of your medical course to get an extra degree or even a PhD (some schools, like Nottingham for example, have a BMedSci degree included as part of the 5 year course.) I know several people who took this route and had a great time doing so. I, however, felt that since practising medicine in a hospital was what I had always wanted to do, I did not want to put this off for another year. I don't feel greatly disadvantaged by choosing this route and it certainly feels good to be earning some money while a few of my friends are still slaving away in fifth year.

I am now working as a house officer in a district general hospital, which may not sound as glamorous as working in a big inner-city hospital but I would certainly advise considering it as an option when choosing your first jobs. True, the patient load is smaller, but this means that there are many opportunities that just aren't there in a bigger hospital, like assisting in theatres or getting more involved in the day-to-day management of patients.

A medical degree seems at times like it's never going to end, but looking back it was certainly worth it. I love my job and given the same choices again I wouldn't change a thing."

"Diagnosis is not the end, but the beginning of practice."

Martin H. Fischer

Chapter 6

Interviews

According to figures from medical schools approximately one third of applicants are interviewed and around half of those interviewed gain an offer for a place. As you are allowed to use up to four of your UCAS choices on medical places, this means that you have a good chance of getting to the vital interview. If you do manage to get an interview then congratulate yourself as you have done really well to catch the eye of the admissions tutor. Now it is up to you to make all the effort you have made up to now count by getting an offer for a place. You will need to think and prepare ahead so that the 15-20 minutes you spend in the interview will show your enthusiasm, commitment and suitability to study medicine.

The majority of medical schools will interview before they offer a place. There are a couple of exceptions to this rule, with Southampton and Edinburgh medical schools not usually interviewing school leavers (though from 2011 Southampton will be interviewing these applicants). The policy towards mature, graduate and international students may be different, so it is best to check directly with the medical school. Some people may be tempted to apply to a particular medical school primarily because they do not interview. This is probably a bad reason to apply for a particular place, firstly because you will need to get used to presenting yourself in a professional environment and secondly because lots of people will have the same idea and there is usually a higher volume of applications for these schools. Of course, if you are attracted to these schools for other reasons then go ahead and apply, and make sure that your personal statement is tip-top.

6.1 Why Bother Interviewing?

The reason that many universities interview candidates rather than just offering a place on the basis of your UCAS form is many-fold. First of all, most universities use it as a way of verifying that you actually wrote the personal statement yourself rather than getting your parents or a friend to do it for you. Some universities explicitly state this on the criteria for assessing applicants. The interviews are face-to-face with you and a panel of interviewers so everything you say is directly from you. This may seem a bit of a cynical reason for interviewing, but the temptation for people to get too much help from someone else is certainly strong as competition for the places increases. Some students may be tempted to ask someone else, who has a better command of language perhaps, to fill in their form, or maybe say they have done things that they haven't. This can be obvious on the day of the interview, so be sure the content and style of your application reflects you and your experience.

The interview is also their chance to assess your ability to think under pressure and communicate, both of which are vital skills for doctors. They recognise that everyone is going to be nervous on the day of their interview so might not be as fluent as normal, but they need to know you are not going to descend into a gibbering wreck when under pressure!

6.2 Countdown to Interview: How to Prepare for the Big Day

If you do get an interview, you should expect it to take place from November to March, although the vast majority take place after Christmas. Oxbridge (Oxford and Cambridge Universities) tend to interview in December. You should have a couple of weeks notice about when and where the interview will take place, but do not panic if you have less time than this. The secret is to do a basic amount of preparation in advance, and to spend the last week or so before the interview familiarising yourself with the specific university and course you are being interviewed for.

Lots of students increase their reading of a newspaper or scientific magazine in the run up to the interview. This cannot be a bad thing, but interviewers will notice if your knowledge of the news or scientific advances only extends to last week! Try to keep an eye on a particular topic that you are interested in, and perhaps how it is developing over time. If you have mentioned a topic of interest in your personal statement then it is foolish not to be well informed about it. You do not need to be an expert, but you might find it useful to learn some basic science that underpins the issue, and its impact on the scientific and general population. Some examples of this will follow in this chapter.

6.3 Mock Interviews

In the weeks leading up to the interview try to arrange some 'mock interviews' with careers teachers or other appropriate people. You may be lucky enough to have a family friend who is a doctor, or a health professional that you met at your work experience that you may be able to ask. This will allow you to get used to talking about yourself and about scientific issues. It is best to practice with people that you do not know well so that you are not too relaxed. You should focus on going through the motions of the interview so you are familiar with the routine on the day. This will mean you are more likely to relax and concentrate on what you are being asked, rather than being distracted by the environment. Remember to get feedback on how your mock interview went. Ask for both good and bad points so you can improve on the next occasion. If it is possible to arrange it, nothing gives you better feedback than having someone video you during your mock interview so that you can assess your own performance.

6.4 The Interview Panel

The majority of medical schools have a similar format for interviews with a panel of two or three interviewers, often from different backgrounds (e.g. one lecturer and one clinical doctor). A number of universities have a current senior medical student on the panel as well so don't be thrown if one of the interviewers doesn't look much older than you do! Most schools will have you do one interview with this panel lasting 20 to 30 minutes during which you will cover a range of topics. Oxford and Cambridge interviews vary between colleges but usually they put you through two 20 minute interviews with different panels, one of which tends to focus more on academic questions and the other on more personal ones.

6.5 Questionnaires and Written Work

A few medical schools such as Cambridge and Nottingham ask applicants to complete a questionnaire prior to the interview. The purpose of these varies between medical schools, but they generally want to know more specific academic results than they would otherwise have available and to ask for evidence that you have the attributes that are required in a doctor.

For ideas to help answer the latter look at the Good Medical Practice guide on the GMC's website:

www.gmc-uk.org

Others will include some written work or give you written information on the day of the interview which you will then have to discuss after a period of time to digest it. Topics covered in these tasks are usually similar to those in our sample interview questions below so there is not much extra preparation that can be done for these.

6.6 Alternative Styles of Interview

A few medical schools have, in recent years, scrapped the traditional interview in favour of other methods of assessment. The University of East Anglia and St. Georges have moved to an OSCE (Objective Structured Clinical Examination) format similar to that used for medical school exams and medical job interviews. This involves rotating around a series of stations, each with a different interviewer, lasting 5-10 minutes each with a different task. Some stations deal with fairly standard interview topics so at one you may be asked to talk through your UCAS personal statement and at another you may be asked to talk about why you want to become a doctor.

At other stations, however, you may have to read a scenario before going in and then be prepared to discuss it, or you may be asked to interact with an actor to test your interpersonal skills. It is possible that this style of interview may spread to other medical schools in the future as it allows assessment of applicants in a very structured, reproducible manner.

The key with this type of interview is to have a very short memory and put any bad stations out of your mind to treat each new station as a completely clean slate, and to remember that if you really don't get on with an examiner at least you will get a different one in only a few minutes!

6.7 The Questions

Although medical schools try to keep their interviews as varied as possible, the vast majority follow a similar format. One can divide common interview questions into several broad categories:

1. **Questions that you <u>must</u> prepare an answer for**

These questions are so likely to come up at interview that it would be foolish not to have thought about them in advance. They are nice as they help you to settle into the interview. For example, if you are able to confidently answer why you want to study medicine and why at that university, you will be less flustered when you are asked a question that requires a spontaneous answer because you will feel more in your stride.

2. **Questions which you will be expected to know quite a bit about from either your A-level syllabus or from your work experience**

Hard to prepare for specifically so you need to rely on the academic ability that has got you through all of your exams to this point. Questions about scientific topics are often then expanded to move into the next type of question.

3. **Questions to take you out of your comfort zone**

You will inevitably get this type of question at interview and these are the ones people tend to complain about afterwards! What the interviewer is trying to do is to test your ability to cope with novel problems and work through them by extrapolating your current knowledge and applying it appropriately. It is important, when faced with a question to which there is not an immediate answer, to avoid getting flustered or panicky. There is no such thing as an impossible interview question, but you will need to take a moment to think it over before answering. It's often quite good to talk through your thought process so they can see where you are going with your answer and they may even offer subtle guidance to keep you on the right track.

4. Questions that can trip you up

There are certain questions which offer you the potential to really put your foot in it if you just blurt out the first thing that comes into your head. We will see a few examples of this later in the chapter.

5. Questions which open up a debate

Here there is no such thing as **the** correct answer. You need to show an appreciation of both sides of an argument and discuss them rationally. Questions on ethical topics commonly fall into this category.

It is these latter few types of questions that will make you stand out from the other students and make the interviewers remember you at the end of a day when they have seen many very similar applicants. Remember that they are looking for people that they are going to have to teach for the next few years so if they admit students who can think through problems rationally and hold reasoned debates their lives will be far more interesting as well.

6.8 The Day of the Interview

On the day of the interview you are likely to wake up at least a little nervous. It is a good idea to decide on and prepare what you intend to wear the night before. Male interviewees should wear a suit or a smart pair of trousers, shirt and tie. Girls should try to look smart, so avoid jeans and do not reveal too much flesh. Try and avoid the temptation to go out and buy a suit especially, but as a general rule try to wear something that the average granny would think you look nice in! You will need to be able to dress appropriately as a doctor so it is important to make a good impression.

You should re-read and familiarise yourself with your personal statement on the day of the interview. In fact, you should know it back to front if at all possible as it is highly likely that it will provide the skeleton for the interview. You should be able to elaborate on all the main points and try to relate them back to your desire to study medicine. Make sure you also know the basics of the course and university to which you are applying and ensure you have read the prospectus.

6.9   The Interview Itself

So eventually the time will come, you'll find yourself sitting there outside the door of the interview room waiting as they finish with the candidate before you. You'll be looking good in your smart clothes, all the points in your personal statement will be fresh in your mind, you'll have brushed up on topical issues and you will have done practice interviews until they seem routine. Your preparation will be brilliant. And yet your stomach will likely still be trying to turn itself inside out, your palms will be sweaty and you'll be wondering if faking a heart attack is a reasonable means of avoiding having to go through the interview. This is <u>normal</u>. It's a small comfort but everyone else will feel just as bad! What you need to be able to do is to put on a bit of an act and come across with an air of confidence and composure despite the butterflies. We don't expect to be able to teach you everything you need to know about how this is done in the space of a few pages – entire books have been written on this very subject. However, what follows are a few condensed tips and pointers that might get you heading in the right direction.

First Impressions Count

It all starts from the moment that you walk through the door and before you have even said a word. It's here that the non-verbal communication kicks in as they will form an instant impression of you in about the first five seconds based on appearance and body language – do you look like a deer in the headlights who will crumble under the pressure of medical school or do you look calm, collected and ready to take whatever is thrown at you? It is not that medical school interviewers are particularly superficial types who moonlight as style critics for fashion magazines. It's just human nature. We all make subconscious snap judgements about people every day without realising it and admissions tutors are no different. If they look at you and subconsciously decide that you look like a professional, like someone who could be a doctor, then you are already part of the way to getting a place and you have not even opened you mouth yet! While they will revise and refine this initial impression as the interview progresses it always pays to have a good starting point.

The first way to score points is to walk in confidently, standing tall with your shoulders back and make sure you keep your head up and give them a friendly smile. Make eye contact from the start as it will mark you out as being both confident in what you are saying and open and trustworthy at the same time. Slinking in and avoiding eye contact by staring at your shoes will have the opposite effect and either make you appear excessively shy or evasive and dishonest. The interviewers may offer to shake your hand and if they do, take their hand in a confident grip for a short shake but avoid any temptation to squeeze the life out of their hand in a misguided attempt to seem confident. If they do not go to shake your hand don't consider this a bad sign or rude. It may simply be that you are the hundredth candidate they have seen that day and they simply can't face having their hands shaken from their

84

wrists for the umpteenth time. It is good etiquette to wait to be offered a seat rather than just diving for the first empty chair you see. Remember that you are in the interview panels' territory so respect that it is their space. If an offer of a seat is not made then take the initiative and politely enquire as to where they would like you to sit. This demonstrates good manners and a respect for the panel that will stand you in good stead for the rest of the interview.

Body Language

Once seated, try to think about your body language as it will project an impression of your attitude towards the interviewers and the interview process as a whole. You don't want to appear overly cocky and laid back as though the interview is no big deal to you, so don't slouch back in the chair, but equally you don't want to seem so stressed that you are fixed rigid to attention. Ideally sit up straight but with a slight body lean towards the interviewer as this suggests that you are focused on what they are saying and are taking an interest in it. Try to avoid the temptation of crossing your arms or legs; although this may feel comfortable it also creates a physical and psychological barrier between you and the panel. Remember you want to appear as 'open' as possible with nothing to hide.

When nervous we all have an inherent tendency to start performing strange stereotyped actions. It just seems to be hardwired into the human psyche. Are you a foot-tapper? Do you play with your hair, fiddle with your face, scratch your backside? (OK, hopefully not that last one) It's a good idea to use your mock interviews to try to find out what your particular nervous tic is so you can work out how to best keep it under control in the real thing. This can be very hard to achieve as it will have been ingrained over the course of your life, but if you have at least identified what you tend to do then that's half of the battle already won. If your annoying habit happens to be something you do with your hands it can be useful to involve them in what you are saying as it both emphasises the points you are making and stops them from getting up to mischief. Great big, theatrical arm waving is not needed, just gentle gestures with open palms (which again suggests openness and honesty) to accentuate your statements.

What You Actually Say

Last, but by no means least, is your speech itself. You will be doing most of the talking in the interviews so unfortunately your voice has plenty of time to portray just how nervous you are unless you are careful to keep it under control. There is a tendency for our speech to speed up when nervous and this is not only a dead giveaway to interviewers, but also means that your mouth may start working faster than your brain, resulting in all sorts of ill-advised statements potentially slipping out. Our best advice would be to pause and take the time to compose your answers before opening your mouth, then to speak slowly and clearly so that your answer is more understandable and so you have time to compose the next part of your answer while you are still talking. Again, doing mock interviews can help train you to do this well.

There's clearly a lot to think about and the process of becoming a good interviewee is not easy for most people. The old adage that practice makes perfect really is applicable here, however, and doing mock interviews can be one of the most effective ways of assessing the areas you need to work on and improve. Even the real interviews themselves are an opportunity to improve. They might not all go according to plan, but if after a bad one you take the time to think through what went well and what needs to be changed rather than going off into a strop, you will be that much stronger the next time round.

6.9 Sample Questions

1. Why do you want to be a doctor/study medicine?

If you have not thought seriously about an answer to this question before going in to any medical school interview then I'm sorry, give up now because there is just no hope for you! In reality of course you will have thought about this question while deciding what course to apply for and writing your personal statement, but in the interview you have to have a succinct, snappy answer to this question which can actually be very difficult to come up with on the spot.

The trouble is that your interviewers will have asked this same question to literally hundreds of applicants over the years so it's very difficult to come up with something original to say. Bland answers along the lines of "I'm interested in science and I want to help people" may be very honest but they are not going to make you stand out from the crowd in any way.

A far more interesting answer thinks about what first grabbed you, what continues to inspire you. Think back to your first real contact with the healthcare profession, was it as a patient, seeing how a relative was treated, do you have relatives who are doctors, or was it through the media? Was there something that struck you, that first made you think you wanted to find out more about being a doctor? You can then go on to talk about what you have done to find out more about being a doctor, how you have convinced yourself that this is what you want to do and how you can demonstrate your commitment to follow this through and fight your way through all the hard work that lies ahead of you.

A large part of this latter process might be the work experience that you have done and that is usually a good direction to steer the conversation as you can demonstrate that you have seen firsthand what the job involves, perhaps you have even discussed with doctors their experiences of medical training.

Above all you need to show that you know what you are getting yourself into, that you are willing to put the work in and above all you need to get across your enthusiasm for medicine as a subject.

Have a look back at the chapters 'Why Medicine?' (Chapter 1) and 'Applications' (Chapter 4) for some further ideas for answers to this question.

2. **You mention that you spent time doing............ in your personal statement. Can you tell us about this and how it affected your decision to apply to medical school?**

You should fully expect that what you have written on your personal statement is likely to shape at least some of the questions thrown your way. As mentioned earlier, this is in part to check that what has been written is your own work, but it's also generally considered fairly comfortable ground for some of the early exchanges of an interview. Knowing this is important to you for two reasons.

First of all, it is clearly vital for you to have read and reread your own personal statement before going in to the interview so you have it clear in your mind.

Secondly, it also means that if you are clever in the writing of your personal statement you can include enticing little snippets in it which they are likely to pick up on that you can then expand on in the interview to show off your broader knowledge of the subject. For example, Heléna mentioned attending a teaching session where she saw a CT (computed tomography) scan of a patient with Cystic Fibrosis on her personal statement and this prompted a number of further questions during her interviews, all on a subject that she had taken the time to research and was able to speak comfortably and knowledgably on.

3. What do you think makes a good doctor?

We have touched on some of the requirements to be a good doctor in earlier chapters so hopefully you will have an idea of some of the things you would want to put in an answer to this question. If we distil out some of the essentials, the most important trait for a doctor is that he/she genuinely cares for his patients, realises that their wellbeing is always at the centre of anything we do and is willing to put in the work to make a difference to their outcome. In addition to hard work this also requires efficiency as there will always be too many patients and too few hours in the day.

Regardless of the specialty that they choose, doctors will be working within a team of professionals so it is essential to have the ability to work well and communicate effectively with colleagues. Obviously there is a lot to learn in medicine and doctors are often faced with quite complex problems so a degree of intelligence is essential. However, they should also possess excellent communication skills thus enabling them to explain diseases and treatments in a straightforward way that patients will be able to understand. Technical skill is vital in a number of specialties, and an interest in teaching and research is important in most branches of medicine.

A doctor who can tick all of those boxes probably has some right to feel quite smug, but the final quality that a doctor needs is humility; to be a safe practitioner a doctor has to understand his limitations and to recognise when the time has come to ask for help from colleagues in the interests of providing the patient with the best possible care.

4. When you think about becoming a doctor, what do you look forward to most and least?

The answer to this sort of question is very individual. We all have aspects of the job that appeal to us but they are different for every doctor. Maybe if you are an aspiring hospital specialist it could be the investigative challenge of making a diagnosis or the technical challenge of intricate surgery. Perhaps the constant variety of work and the long term relationship with patients that you get in general practice is what attracts you. Or is it the continuing learning opportunities presented throughout your career, or the opportunities for research that really get you excited? As with most questions asked at interview, your answer will be much stronger if you are able to relate it back to something you have seen or experienced during your work-experience placements. It makes for a more convincing answer to be able to say, for example, "I look forward to developing the technical skills required to be an excellent cardiologist, especially after having the opportunity to observe a stent placement in a heart patient during my hospital placement," rather than not being able to justify or qualify your decisions and preferences.

The second half of the question, what do you least look forward to, is actually far more tricky and you need to tread carefully here. You have to come up with some sort of negative; you can't just ignore the question. At the same time you really need to avoid criticising some core part of the job of a doctor. So to say, for example, "I really don't want to work nights because I'll be scared of being responsible for all those patients on my own and, besides, I need my beauty sleep," will lose you a ton of points because that's something that you have to be prepared to do as a doctor. Far better would be to pick something more peripheral to talk about here. For example, "I think I may be frustrated when the politics of medicine and government targets interfere with the care that I can give my patients or affect staff morale." This kind of answer shows that you are super keen but recognise that external pressures can, and do, affect a doctor's ability to get on with the job.

5. **What personal qualities/strengths do you have which would make you a good doctor? Can you think of any weaknesses that you think you would like to work on?**

The ability to analyse oneself is a desirable trait in doctors because when lives are at stake you need to be able to recognise your limitations, and also you need an awareness of your weak points so you can work on becoming a better doctor. Consequently, you should not feel too uncomfortable about pointing out some of your weaknesses to your interviewers, as you are showing that you have the potential to improve. Just don't slag yourself off too much and make sure you spend considerably longer stressing your good points!

6. **Can you think of a team situation where your communication skills have been vital? Tell us about the situation and your contribution.**

This is a really crucial skill for doctors to have so they may ask you about it directly in addition to assessing how you communicate with them during the interview. Poor communication is the number one reason for patient dissatisfaction, poor compliance with the treatments that you prescribe, and for complaints and legal action. Effective communication is also the most important ingredient for good teamwork with other doctors, nurses and other staff. In answering this question try to show that you appreciate this and use an example of a specific time when your good communication skills made the best of a difficult situation, brought your team together for a common goal or, in some way, altered the outcome for the better. You can then contrast this with what might have happened had you not communicated so effectively.

It may also be useful to identify and expand on any examples of effective communication you saw in practice during your work-experience placements. For example, you may have seen a doctor discussing a patient's complicated condition with a colleague and then witnessed the same doctor effectively explaining the same condition to the patient and discussing treatment options, in language that anyone can understand. This ability to switch from talking 'medicalese' to normal English is a key skill and the medics who are adept at it are particularly good at communicating with their patients. If that same doctor had simply bamboozled their patient with an avalanche of medical jargon then the chances are that the patient would not have followed the treatment plan effectively, would have felt uninvolved in their own care, and may even have ended up resenting their doctor.

Oh, and of course, most people will not say when they don't understand something, for fear of looking stupid or not wanting to appear rude, so a good doctor will check that their patients are genuinely following and understand what is being discussed with them.

Keep an eye out for this type of communication skill the next time you're on a work-experience placement.

7. **What are your outside interests and hobbies? Tell me about a non-academic project that you were involved in.**

Medical schools like 'well rounded' people who are going to be able to relate to their patients so this type of question is common. The important thing in answering this type of question is to relate the transferable skills that you have developed in these projects to their use in your medical career. For example, if you were captain of the rugby team you will have gained many of the leadership and teamwork skills that all doctors need. If you were on any club committees then you will have learned a great deal about organisation and time management. Whatever it is you do and have done in the past there is probably some aspect of it that you can use as a good example of a skill that will prove useful as a doctor.

As well as demonstrating a range of transferable skills, showing that you have extracurricular interests and hobbies also demonstrates to the interview panel that you are the kind of sociable person who will:

a) contribute to the medical community and engage with your fellow classmates and lecturers, and

b) have something to take your mind off academic rigour occasionally, an important mechanism for coping with the unavoidable stress and pressures of being on one of the toughest courses there is.

Medical faculties, and the wider medical profession, do not want the medics of tomorrow to be broken, hyper-stressed, nervous wrecks, at any point during their training or their careers so if you can show them that you are able to switch off once in a while and do something non-medical that you genuinely enjoy and get pleasure from then you will go a long way to satisfying them that you have the tools to succeed in the profession.

8. **What have you done on work experience? Was there anything that particularly surprised/interested you? OR Can you tell me about a condition or disease that you learnt about on work experience?**

Work experience is an area of great interest to the interviewers. As mentioned in the 'Work Experience' chapter, what they want to see is not just that you turned up to do it but that you actually interacted and bothered to think about what you were seeing. With this in mind try, when you do work experience placements, pick up on a few specific diseases that you have seen and do a little extra reading about them on websites such as **www.patient.co.uk** or ask one of the doctors about them and jot down a few notes. You don't need to know any great detail, just some of the basics about the sort of symptoms and problems the patient may have come in with, what was done to diagnose the disease (blood tests, scans etc), and how the doctors were treating it (drugs or surgery, for example).

9. Have you read our Medical School prospectus? What appealed to you about the course here?

This question is not put in purely to inflate the egos of the admissions tutors who will obviously feel that their course is fantastic. You need to show why this particular course in this particular university stands out to you above all the others on offer. Try to pick out the unique features that make it different, perhaps in the structure of the teaching, any components of the course that are not on offer elsewhere or any impressive or brand new teaching facilities that they are obviously proud of. Basically, whatever really stands out. It is worth noting that several of the 'newer' medical schools are very proud of their youth and make reference to it in their prospectus. In general the benefits of these courses centre around their ability to design a course which closely follows the most recent GMC guidance on teaching methods without being encumbered by entrenched 'traditional' didactic teaching methods that lecturers may be reluctant to get rid of. This should mean that graduates are more attuned to medicine as it is today.

Also try to talk about other aspects of life at that university and in that city. Perhaps you have spoken to current students and like the friendly atmosphere, have looked into clubs or societies that you might join, thought about where you will be living and what life will be like.

Remember that they will be looking for people who will fit in and enjoy university life as you will be living there for a number of years.

10. What do you think are the advantages and disadvantages of a PBL course? Why do you think a PBL course will suit you personally?

If you apply to a course that teaches medicine using the PBL (Problem Based Learning) approach then you may be asked this question. This tests your understanding of the teaching method as it is likely to be very different from what you have experienced at school. We have already talked about the basics of this style of teaching in earlier chapters and we refer you back for a refresh of the salient points.

In answer to the second half of the question try to give examples of times you have shown an ability to research topics in depth and discuss your findings with others, perhaps in projects you have done at school or extracurricular activities such as debating groups. It is also important to show an appreciation that you will develop skills in PBL sessions such as team working, presentation and teaching which are going to be needed throughout your medical career.

11. Can you tell me about a significant recent advance in medicine or science? Why has this interested you?

OR

Can you tell us about any significant medical stories in the media at the moment?

We mentioned earlier that you need to keep an eye on the press for the few months prior to the interview. You should by now be interested enough in the subject that you are noticing these stories without trying too hard but if you take time to do a little extra research in scientific publications, which can usually be done in minutes online, you can look far more impressive as you can show you have been able to form your own opinions rather that just buying into tabloid propaganda!

Interviewers can't expect you to read every article in every paper so they are only likely to ask you about the big national stories that run throughout the media for an extended period and ones like the 'Hospital Superbug' stories that they keep coming back to from time to time. Have a look in our 'Topical Issues' chapter for the sort of thing you will be expected to have come across.

It is worth asking parents, grannies, etc. to cut out any medical stories that they come across from now on and to start making a little scrapbook of clippings that you can skim through before interviews to at least give the impression that you have been following these stories for months and months! If you have any friends from years above you already at medical school you might ask them to forward their copies of the Student BMJ (which they get sent monthly if they sign up with the British Medical Association) as this gives you a view of some of the stories from a more medical perspective, without all the stuffy scientific style of other journals.

12. What do you consider to be important advances in medicine over the last 50 / 100 years?

A really fascinating question if you take the time to think about it as you could take a number of completely different approaches, all equally impressive. The most obvious answers will focus on major breakthroughs in the science of medicine, many of which have had widespread implications across a range of medical specialties. There is no shortage of such advances from which to choose, from the first use of ether to induce anaesthesia in 1846, making the practice of surgery more humane, through to Lister's 1867 principles of asepsis which dramatically help reduce surgical mortality, or Röentgen's discovery of X-rays in 1895. The last 100 years saw Fleming's discovery of penicillin and the birth of antibiotics, the introduction of national vaccination programmes and our ability to manipulate the immune system and transplant organs. There is probably no need for you to be able to quote the names of the doctors and scientists who are credited with the breakthroughs but you should have a general idea of why they had such a huge impact.

One could also take a political tack and talk about the birth of the NHS, replacing a haphazard group of private practices with a nationalised service which remains free at the point of contact for all patients. The recent debates over healthcare reforms in the United States make this as topical as ever.

The other way to answer this question, particularly if you are a budding surgeon, is to turn the question on its head and show how little has changed in the last hundred years in many fields. If you visit the museums in the Royal College of Surgeons in London and Surgeon's Hall in Edinburgh, one of the most striking things that you will see is how similar many of the surgical instruments of 150 years ago are to those used today. Of course our instruments today may be made out of plastic rather than carved from ivory and they may all be disposable rather than being handed down through the generations, but the form of the instruments and the principles of surgery have undergone more of a gradual evolution than a major leap forwards.

13. What will be the major advances in medicine in the next 50 years? Will the Human Genome Project advance medical practice?

The Human Genome Project was a massive international undertaking which sought to identify and map the 25,000 genes which make up the

Human genome at the cost of around $3 billion. They produced the first complete copy of the genome in 2003 and at the time it was hailed as ushering in a new era of medicine, with gene therapy being able to target many diseases at their roots in the DNA. While the detailed maps of the genome have aided researchers in identifying the genes associated with many inherited conditions and developing tests for them, we have yet to see the much anticipated explosion of very specifically targeted drugs and gene therapy for medical conditions known to have a genetic basis. You might like to have a think about how we could target and manipulate particular genes. If and when these therapies do appear they could have an enormous impact on the practice of medicine but at the moment we will just have to wait and see.

14. Use the graph given and your own knowledge to explain why death rates from infectious diseases fell in the twentieth century.

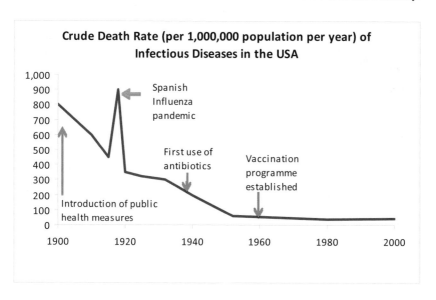

Interviewers may use data to open up debate. The graph above is designed to give you a taster of this sort of question. When you are given a piece of data such as a graph you will be tested on your ability to systematically analyse and then critique a trend. What this means in layman's terms is not immediately jumping in to a premature explanation of what might be happening, but to stand back and look at exactly what is being presented. This is a really important skill for doctors who need to collate information and then make decisions about patients.

In the case of this specific graph you should take a few moments to observe, without resorting to verbal diarrhoea. For example many students may immediately say that antibiotics or vaccines are the main factor, without looking at the graph. Introduce the title and the axis, making a note of the scale. You may well notice something that otherwise would have tripped you up. Then go on to describe the trend. For example in this graph, "crude death rates from infectious disease in the USA decreases from 1900 to around 1918, where there is a spike in death rates. Death rates then fall to the current day." You can then move on to suggesting reasons for the trend. The graph shows that death rates were falling before the introduction of antibiotics and vaccines, seemingly because of improvements in public health. Examples of these include improving sanitation and reducing overcrowding. The spike is due to an influenza pandemic. You may also want to comment on how reliable the data is. How might it be misleading? How was the data collected? May there be other factors not accounted for? Is data from the USA applicable to the UK and the rest of the world? If you can go beyond the standard answers that a lot of your peers will launch blindly into then you will go a long way towards impressing the interview panel with your ability to think logically and analyse calmly.

15. If you were to design yourself as a bacterium, what would your main aims be and how would you achieve this?

This sort of question would take most applicants out of their comfort zone. It requires a deep breath and some logical thinking, as well as a bit of imagination. Remember, in this sort of question interviewers are looking at how you respond to a question you don't immediately know the answer to. So don't panic! Don't give up! Maybe say "that's an interesting question I haven't thought about before." Then try to break down the question in to manageable parts. The knowledge you *need* will be really simple, pre-GCSE even. In this example, the principle is that bacteria generally aim to multiply. Now you would need to come up with a couple of ideas of how they do this. One thing to reassure you is that the interviewer will help you along the way with some hints or tips if you get stuck, and almost all will!

Bacteria can spread within or between people. Within the body a bacteria may be able to move into an area with no competition such as swim into the sterile urethra or cross into the blood stream. They may target an area with lots of available nutrition, such as the gastrointestinal system. Once here they need to evade the host's immune response. They may also be resistant to antibiotics, meaning they can multiply in these sites. Bacteria can release substances to aid spread between people (infectivity) by causing symptoms, like diarrhoea. Entering a sterile environment from which they cannot spread (such as the brain) would not be useful for infectivity and so it is rare.

You may have struck gold and be able to sprinkle in some examples from your reading or A level course. For example, the fact that *Proteus* uses a flagellum to swim up the urethra, or that *Chlamydia* lives within cells to evade the host. You should know a bit about antibiotic resistance and MRSA, and would be able to mention this if you are tackling this point. The main thing to emphasise is to be determined, but listen to direction from the interviewer, and try to stay systematic in your answer.

16. You are a junior doctor on a ward round. The consultant has just told off a colleague over a minor point and seems upset. What should you do?

This question is essentially trying to gauge two things: your ability to see both sides of an argument and to be caring towards other people. In answering this question you may want to show that you understand mistakes made by doctors can be dangerous, but that feedback should not be destructive or intimidating. You should try to stay professional, but realise that your colleague may need support. After all, it may be you next time that needs a shoulder to cry on! If you think the behaviour is repeating itself or destructive, you might want to speak to an allocated, more senior person to raise your concerns so that the issue can be resolved. After all, the consultant is likely to be extremely busy and may not be aware that they are damaging the work of the team around them.

17. What symptoms might a person with bone cancer have?

You don't need to have read specifically about this condition to make sensible suggestions to this answer. In fact, if the examiner senses you have read about it, they may move swiftly on. You are likely to be assessed on your reasoning skills, rather than whether you can regurgitate a textbook you happened to have read. You should be able to use your knowledge of what bones do and how they are structured to work out what happens if they are diseased. If you give a logical answer, you will gain credit, even if it's not actually the 'correct' answer.

Bones function as skeletal support for muscles to attach to and as protection to organs such as the lungs or to bone marrow. They have a good blood supply and are innervated by many nerves. Long bones grow from the ends, at sites called epiphyseal (growth) plates. Bones are made from a matrix of proteins and also contain calcium and phosphate. From these facts you should be able to work out that if cancer of the bone causes changes in their structure it may weaken the bone and cause fractures, as well as causing local pain and swelling. As bones grow from plates near their ends, cancers which originate in the bone often begin here, where cells are dividing. Large tumours near to joints may limit movement.

Additionally, many cancers from elsewhere in the body can spread (metastasise) to bone in the bloodstream. In some cases the cancer may cause bone to break down, which causes the release of calcium into the blood. In other cases the local pressure effects of a growing tumour or the fractures they cause may compress nearby structures, such as nerves and the spinal cord. This may cause specific nervous symptoms, such as muscle weakness, or loss of certain reflexes, and pain.

As well as these specific symptoms, a patient may experience more general symptoms such as weight loss and malaise. As cancer metastasises to other tissues, the patient may experience symptoms related to the function of those tissues.

18. What do you think are the sorts of problems facing a person with a chronic health problem, such as difficulty breathing?

This is a very common topic to be explored in the first year of many medical courses so it is sensible to have an idea about it in case it pops up in the interviews. Clearly any long-term health problem will present its own set of specific medical problems but you will not be expected to know any details of these at this stage. Instead, you need to show some understanding of the effect that a chronic disease will have on aspects of life that most of us take for granted. For instance, depending on the symptoms of the disease and the number of hospital visits that are necessary it may be very difficult to hold down a regular job leading to serious financial problems. They may become socially isolated if they have difficulties getting out of their house, and never forget that their condition can seriously affect the lives of the families as well as their own. These stresses can be very difficult to cope with and lead to high rates of depression in this group of patients, something we are now becoming better at screening for. The ability to think beyond the immediate medical problem and to take a more holistic approach to treating patients has been one of the core values of general practice since the inception of the specialty, but is now becoming a larger focus within medical school teaching.

19. How do you think the internet has influenced the practice of medicine?

Although many doctors would say that the internet is fast becoming the bane of their lives we often overlook how useful it can be. In this day and age we know so much about so many conditions, but very rarely do we have the time to sit down with a patient and impart all this information to them. In a 10 minute consultation you might be able to get across three or four important points - any more than that and none of it will sink in. So to be able to give a patient the address of a website which has all the information that they could need for them to browse at their own pace is hugely valuable. Many patient support websites also have contact groups where patients with rarer conditions can find out how other sufferers are coping with the condition.

The problems occur because the information available on the internet is essentially unregulated and filled with misinformation which can undermine patients belief in their doctors and in some cases leads to patients demanding treatments for bizarre illnesses which they clearly don't have but which their computer has told them about. The key point with this question is to identify the pros and cons and to then, perhaps, offer your own opinion.

20. What do you think of nurses developing extended roles and undertaking tasks previously done by doctors?

At times this can prove a contentious issue. Take care not to come across as arrogant or overly critical of other professionals when answering questions like this. The fact is that good nursing staff, who are able to take on jobs previously done by doctors, can greatly improve the efficiency of a unit. For example, a well trained practice nurse who can do patients' regular asthma or diabetes checkups can free up a GP to see more complicated cases.

The concern arises mainly in the hospital environment where there is the risk that junior doctors will become deskilled if nurses are performing procedures for them, in combination with their reduced hours under the European Working Time Directive. This has been the focus of a number of recent articles in the medical media.

21. Do you think medicine should be more about changing behaviour to prevent disease or treating existing disease?

This is perhaps the biggest change in medical practice in the last few decades. Whilst we are getting better and better at managing or treating illnesses and rehabilitating patients after them, our interventions are both expensive and, in many instances, do not quite manage to fully return patients back to one hundred percent. An increasing focus is now placed on patient education, aiming to identify and reduce the impact of risk factors and prevent disease in the first place. Secondary prevention, following episodes of disease, is then equally important to prevent recurrence.

Although it might seem like the less sexy side of medicine it promises to be both more cost efficient and better for patients and we are just starting to see the benefits of this new focus. Obviously it takes a lot of effort, especially as the patient needs to fully buy into what you are recommending in order to enable them to make significant changes to their lifestyle. It is therefore important to ensure you polish up those communication skills!

Major examples include the role of sun exposure in cases of skin cancer, and the risk factors associated with heart disease, obesity and Type 2 diabetes.

22. Do you think patient's treatments should be limited by the NHS budget or do they have the right to new therapies no matter what the cost?

A question that could spark a debate lasting for hours in the real world as it is fundamental to the way that the NHS will work in future years. With ever more expensive new drugs and procedures becoming available and a finite NHS budget, it almost gets to the point where in order to fund one patient having some high priced new drug, cuts are required to be made elsewhere. This may result in other patients missing out on their treatment.

Unfortunately, although the National Institute for Health and Clinical Excellence (NICE) has a specific remit to analyse the cost effectiveness of new medical technology and decide if they will be funded on the NHS, the media and public opinion can often browbeat management into providing drugs against NICE recommendations.

A good recent example is the drug trastuzumab (Herceptin) for breast cancer, which was not initially available on the NHS due to its extreme cost and limited effect on overall survival. After a series of very public campaigns by cancer sufferers and debates at the highest levels of the courts and government a number of NHS trusts were forced to provide Herceptin to specific patients and ultimately a decision was made to change the guidelines and make the drug available despite the financial implications.

Again, try to identify the various sides of the argument and then offer your own, reasoned opinion.

23. **You have one liver available for transplant, but three patients all with equal need for a transplant.**

    1. **One is an ex-alcoholic middle aged man with cirrhosis.**

    2. **The second a single mother with two young children who has taken a paracetamol overdose while suffering post-natal depression.**

    3. **The third a 5 year old with an inherited liver abnormality.**

    How would you decide to whom it should be given?

This is a way of asking about allocation of scarce resources on a smaller-scale than the previous question. In this question all of the patients have the same need for the resource (i.e. the liver) as all will ultimately die without it. It may be that one is closer to death than the others so could be perceived as having a more 'urgent' need, but this urgency is an inefficient means of allocating resources as we would end up spending disproportionate amounts on dying patients who may have a much lower chance of actually surviving the operation. The chance of success clearly must be considered.

One method used to compare the benefits that each patient would derive is to estimate the number of years which their life would be extended by a successful operation. Using this method the younger patient would obviously usually win, but many inherited conditions can affect multiple organs. What if we were to extend his life knowing that he would then have to live with other long-term disabilities? Should the years of disabled life count for as much as the potentially healthy years of the single mother? Healthcare economists have a unit called a QALY (Quality-Adjusted Life Years) to take this into account, but this opens another can of worms as who are we to say that life with a disability is worth proportionally less?

One could also argue that the single mother and the alcoholic have caused their own liver damage so are less deserving of a second chance but are we right to judge patients in this way? And is it worse to damage your liver with a single overdose or with years of heavy drinking? Finally, does the fact that the single mother has two children dependent on her give her more of a right to resources?

There is really no right answer here so don't expect to arrive at one. In fact, these are such difficult questions that some have suggested that the only fair system for decisions like these is a lottery to give everyone an equal chance.

24. Animals that are clearly suffering are often 'put down'. Should humans who are suffering and wish to die be treated in the same way?

Ouch! This certainly is about as controversial and emotive as it gets so you'll need to tread carefully with difficult ethical questions like this. Definitely take time to plan what you are going to say before you speak because you don't want come across as some reincarnation of Harold Shipman.

The law is very clear on this issue, saying that "it is not lawful for a doctor to administer a drug to his patient to bring about his death, even though that course is prompted by a humanitarian desire to end his suffering" (stated by Lord Goff in the case of Bland vs. Airedale NHS Trust, 1993). However, from an ethical point of view there are certainly issues on either side of the argument which are worthy of debate.

Opponents of euthanasia and physician-assisted suicide can argue that ending a life is intrinsically wrong, that no matter how hopeless a patient's situation may seem there may always be the chance of misdiagnosis or some hope for the invention of a new cure and that good quality palliative care should be able to manage the symptoms of a dying patient.

However, the other side of the argument is that euthanasia has been legalised in a number of other countries under strict controls and various patient groups strongly support the principle. Proponents believe that patients, who have a right to make decisions about their medical treatment, should also have the right to choose the time and manner of their own death when faced with a terminal illness and a painful, undignified demise if nature is allowed to take its course. A growing number of cases have appeared in the newspapers of British patients travelling to clinics in other countries for 'assisted suicide', but this is an expensive option available to very few. One could also point out that withdrawal of life-sustaining treatment and even of artificial means of feeding is legal even though the consequences of this action are clear.

Of course the practical problems of policing euthanasia to avoid abuse of that power, and to ensure that patients consent is entirely voluntary, would make it extremely difficult to implement in the UK, regardless of the outcome of your ethical debate!

6.10   Other Questions You Could Use to Practice

1. Have you seen a film or read a book recently that has made you think? How and why?

2. What are the arguments for and against non-essential surgery being available on the NHS?

3. Should alternative or complimentary medicine be funded by the NHS? Why?

4. Is there any difference between withdrawing life-sustaining treatment and euthanasia? Should there be?

5. If you were the director of a hospital trust and were offered a million pounds to improve the services, how would you spend it and why?

6. Where do you see yourself in 10 years time? What would you like your patients/colleagues to think of you?

7. What do you think about the way doctors are portrayed in the media? How do you think this will affect patients' views of their own doctors?

8. What is your favourite disease and why?

You may be able to think of some suitable practice questions yourself. It is also a good idea to ask any medics you work with on work experience placements, or medical students you know, whether they can think of any. The more you practice answering a variety of questions the more prepared and calm you will ultimately be on the big day of the interviews themselves.

6.11   Your Questions to the Interviewers

It is likely at the end of the interview that they will finish up by asking if there is anything that you would like to ask them before you leave. Too many candidates feel a tremendous pressure to ask something, anything, no matter how inane the question might be. This is just the sort of thing to avoid right at the end as you will leave a lasting bad impression.

Try to look at it this way, if they have done their job properly you should, by then, have just about all the information you need from the prospectus, open day and letters that they have sent you. Asking something to which the answer is readily available in the prospectus will make it look like you have not bothered to do your research before interview, therefore, if no good questions spring to mind, it is useful to have a pre-rehearsed little patter along the lines of:

"That's very kind of you to ask but no, I think all of my questions about the course have been answered at your open day"

as this sounds a lot better than:

"Er...well, er....no"

That said, if you do have a genuinely good question this can be one last chance to impress the interviewers.

One good line of questioning is to ask about fitting extra-curricular activities around the medical course, something along the lines of:

"I currently compete in tiddlywinks at a high level and would like to keep this up with a view to qualifying for the 2012 Olympics but obviously would not want to compromise my medical studies. How would the medical school view this and do you know how other high-level athletes have managed this at your school in the past?"

This both highlights your achievements if they have not already been talked about and shows that you are a planner who has already started thinking about life at their medical school.

Another way to go with this would be to ask them to clarify points regarding specific features of their course, for example:

"I see that your prospectus mentions the possibility of doing X,Y and Z in the later years of the course. How many students are able to do this each year?"

This shows that you have read their prospectus and that you have a particular interest in something which they offer. It also turns the tables to an extent – remember that if you are a good applicant they are selling themselves to you too!

6.12   After The Interview

Although you may feel you have a pretty good idea how things went as soon as you walk out of the interview room, it really is impossible to know how your overall application compares to all the others for that course. Indeed, in the larger medical schools where interviews are spread over a number of days it may be some time before the interviewers themselves know. You therefore face the unpleasant prospect of anxiously waiting at home for a few weeks after the interview before getting a message via UCAS saying what the medical school thinks of you. This will come in the form of either a conditional offer of a place, an unconditional offer (very rarely) or a rejection.

If you get an offer then congratulations, all that preparation has paid off, now you just have to get those pesky A-levels out of the way. If it's a rejection then don't fret, think about what went well and what you need to do better for the next interview. If you have done all of your interviews and still had no good news then this does not mean that it is the end of the road, there are still ways in.

If you have been rejected from all of your applications (or have received offers but declined them) you may be able to apply to courses which still have vacancies between February and June via UCAS Extra. This is admittedly a long shot for a popular subject like medicine but it can't hurt to look on the UCAS website.

You should also remember that some of the schools that interviewed you may have liked you, but simply had too many good applicants to give you a conditional offer. If this is the case then there is a reasonable chance that your name may have been kept on a waiting list, which would give you first dibs on any places that become available via the clearing system once the A-level exam results are published. Some medical schools may be willing to divulge if you have been put on such a list if contacted either by the applicant or their UCAS referee.

Summary

If you are a decent candidate and follow our tips in the previous chapters there is a good chance that you will be asked to at least one interview.

You need to be very aware that at interview you have a very limited time to impress, but fortunately there is almost limitless time to prepare beforehand – make sure you use it! Practice, practice, practice, make sure you know all the topics mentioned on your personal statement off pat, keep an eye on stories in the news and above all try to arrange some mock interviews before the real thing so you are used to the way they work.

During the interview itself try no to get flustered, whatever they throw at you. Remember – there is no such thing as an impossible interview question!

Profile: **Harminder Gill** BSc

Harminder is in the fifth year of the medical course at Oxford and has an intercalated BSc in Physiology and Medical Sciences from UCL. He is the current president of the Hugh Cairns Surgical Society and has raised money for the Hugh Cairns Surgical Foundation, having a keen interest in acute medicine and trauma surgery himself. Harminder enjoys playing squash and captained the UCL medical school team in his second year. He has also performed and choreographed hip-hop routines in several UCL Dance Society shows.

Harminder's Story

"I'm Harminder Gill, a 5th year medical student. I've been lucky enough to attend two great universities in my time as a medical student. I was originally at University College London, UCL, for pre-clinical medicine and now undertake my clinical studies at Oxford University.

I originally applied to UCL for a number of reasons. Firstly, it was a university offering both arts and science courses. This nurtures a vibrant and diverse student body, and means there are always plenty of interesting people around, especially when you fancy a change from other medics! UCL has a strong academic tradition, and you can expect the pre-clinical lecture courses and practical schedule (which is largely computer-based learning) to be intense. The course is 'integrated' which means that you have clinical training focusing on communications skills, ethics and law, and epidemiology alongside the pre-clinical science. The course is 'modular', which means that it is taught in blocks lasting 4-6 weeks, with small breaks in between. It is a systems-based course meaning all the anatomy, physiology, pathology etc. of a given organ or system are given in a lecture course. It was, in the large part, well taught and very interesting. It differs from the more traditional style of course taught in Oxford, Cambridge, Edinburgh and Bristol, where subjects are taught individually, i.e. you would learn pharmacology, physiology and anatomy and other subject all separately. Some prefer this especially if they prefer to learn things separately and put them together in a way that suits their thinking. At UCL integrating a Bachelor's degree is compulsory, but there are plenty to choose from and it gives the opportunity to do a bit of research.

Moving to Oxford for clinical studies was the right choice for me, but an incredibly tough decision. UCL is composed of some amazing hospitals including the world-renowned Great Ormond Street Children's Hospital and Queen's Sq Neurology Hospital. This means that there is a great breadth of clinical exposure to a range of both typical and exotic pathology. This also means that teaching is conducted by inspirational individuals who are leaders in their fields of research. However, UCL is a massive medical school, and it's easy to feel like just a number. Oxford on the other hand is a small medical school, and offers a very personal and tailored experience, including individual career's advice. The teaching is very good and is delivered by the medical school but also by the colleges, which have their own clinical tutors. In addition, there is plenty of opportunity to seek help where required, and many of the consultants are top of their fields. Oxford also offers a certain unique experience of the college lifestyle and various other privileges like dining at formal hall, living in a stunning, historic city, and doing exams in academic dress (not everyone's a fan of this!).

In terms of admissions, my advice would be to focus on the predictable questions: Why medicine? Why the place you're applying to? What makes a good doctor? What are your strengths/weaknesses? Try to be as honest as possible and think carefully about these kinds of topics before your interview. It is often useful to have a good understanding of current medical debate and controversy – the kind that crops up regularly in broadsheet newspapers. In addition most medical schools will ask some kind of ethical question – this is often to gauge your analytical ability to weigh a situation, but also your capacity to think empathically and show compassion. There is often no correct response, so expect to discuss your answer with your interviewers. Finally try to relax and smile!

Whichever medical school you choose, I wish you the best of luck!"

Chapter 7

Topical Issues

What follows are a few brief notes about some of the medical stories which have been in the news in the last 18 months or so, which could potentially crop up for discussion at interview. This is in no way an exhaustive list and we have just scratched the surface of each topic. It's up to you to read around them and form your own opinions.

7.1 Obesity Epidemic

Our standard measure of a person's body habitus is the Body Mass Index (BMI). You can calculate your BMI by dividing your weight in kilograms by the square of your height in meters (kg/m^2). A normal, healthy BMI is defined as 18.5-25 kg/m^2 with scores of 25-30 kg/m^2 classed as overweight and over 30 kg/m^2 as obese. Over the last 30 years there has been an alarming upward trend in BMIs in populations across the globe such that 1 billion people worldwide are now classed as overweight with 300 million of these being obese. This is mainly due to increased consumption of more energy-dense, nutrient-poor foods with high levels of sugar and saturated fats, in combination with reduced levels of physical activity. In Britain almost one in four adults and around 15% of children are now obese.

This epidemic of obesity has huge knock-on effects on health. The metabolic effects of obesity lead to raised blood pressure, cholesterol, triglycerides and insulin resistance, which in turn increases the chances of developing Type 2 Diabetes and coronary heart disease. There are also established links to osteoarthritis, respiratory difficulties, infertility and various types of cancer.

So we have watched this problem developing and the medical world realises how serious it is, but what can we actually do about it? Although in theory the solution would appear to be as simple as encouraging our patients to burn more calories (exercise) and take in fewer calories (healthier diet), this is where things get overly complicated. The fact that there are dozens of diet plans on the market tells us that there remains disagreement among the experts as to exactly what combination of foods is most favourable.

The government has published papers on diet and exercise in schools, how employers could help workers get fit and how manufacturers can reduce fat, sugar and salt in food. However, in the Change4Life campaign launched in 2009, the Chief Medical Officer, amongst others, is advocating a healthier lifestyle with 30 minutes of moderate exercise five times a week and a healthier diet with more fruit and vegetables and lower in fat and sugars. One has to wonder, however, if the message is getting across when schools ban unhealthy 'fast-food' on their school dinner menus and the next day there are pictures on the news of mothers handing hamburgers and fries through the bars of the school gate to their children in protest!

7.2   GP Cover Outside of Normal Working Hours

This subject was thrown into the public's consciousness following the coroner's inquest into the death of 70 year old David Gray who was given a massive overdose of the painkiller diamorphine by a German doctor working his first shift for a British company, which provided out of hours cover for patients of Cambridgeshire GP practices. The doctor was unfamiliar with the painkillers used in this country and so did not realise that he had administered a dose several times in excess of that which was necessary. The incident prompted calls for closer vetting of doctors coming from other countries to work in the UK and for UK general practices to 'take back' the responsibility of caring for their patients at evenings and weekends.

The provision of GP cover at these unsociable times (outside of the 8am to 6:30pm working day) has been an issue since the government agreed to a new GP Contract in 2004 which, among other things, allowed GPs to opt out of being available to see their patients outside of regular working hours. 90% of GP practices took this option leaving a number of private companies and GP consortiums to look after patients with decidedly mixed results. Reports suggest that in some areas of the country a single GP covers a patient population of several hundred thousand at night!

There are now plans to overhaul the system, but we are unlikely to see a return to the pre-2004 days of each GP practice looking after its own patients 24 hours a day. With the increasing complexity of medicine in General Practice it is unrealistic to expect a GP to work through the night and then still be in a fit state to see patients the following morning when hospital doctors are now limited to shifts of no longer than 13 hours to enhance patient safety.

7.3   Slipping Standards in the NHS

Another year, another scandal involving unacceptable standards of care in an NHS hospital. The Mid Staffordshire Foundation Trust is one of the latest to be dragged though the papers following the launch of an official enquiry in 2008 into large numbers of potentially avoidable deaths attributed to inadequate staffing, poor standards of hygiene and a lack of basic nursing care. Stories such as this beg the question of how a group of healthcare professionals can allow the situation to get so bad before action is taken?

120

Have we produced a generation of doctors too highly educated to dirty their hands with the mundane but important tasks? And likewise, by training many more specialist nurses and nurse practitioners, are we creating nurses who are too posh to wash patients? Is the reliance on locum nurses to fill gaps in rotas creating an environment where nurses feel less fidelity to a specific ward and their patients on it? Shouldn't the consultants (who are ultimately responsible for all aspects of the care of their patients) have taken charge? And what does NHS management do exactly? No, seriously, please do enlighten me.

We all have a responsibility to put the care of our patients at the top of our priority list and as junior doctors you will find that you are in a particularly powerful position in this respect with just enough authority to make yourself heard, but also enough time each day physically on the wards (unlike your consultant who may breeze through for only a couple of hours a week on their ward rounds) that you should be aware of any problems that are arising. But equally the management of hospitals need to foster an atmosphere where concerns raised by staff are taken seriously and properly investigated, and where there is no stigma or fear of recrimination for 'whistleblowing.'

7.4 Hospital 'Superbugs'

In the past 10 years we have witnessed the rise of a number of particularly unpleasant pathogens which the press quickly dubbed 'superbugs' due to their resistance to many of our antibiotics and the serious nature of the illnesses that they can cause. Of these the most important are MRSA (methicillin resistant *Staphylococcus aureus*) and *Clostridium difficile*.

MRSA is a strain of the very common *Staphylococcus aureus* bacteria (carried in the nostrils and skin of many of us) which has evolved to become resistant to many of our standard antibiotics. In the majority of cases MRSA causes localised skin and soft tissue infections, but it does have the potential to cause severe systemic illnesses affecting multiple organs. Because it is possible to be a carrier of MRSA without developing symptoms it is not unheard of to become infected with MRSA outside of the hospital environment. Patients in hospital, however, are far more at risk of catching MRSA as wounds, ulcers, catheters and intravenous lines provide a route of entry for MRSA to invade the body. Because in hospital bacteria are usually spread between patients on the hands of doctors and nurses it quickly became a hot topic politically and in the media.

Now that the problem has been identified hospitals are taking strong measures to prevent MRSA entering and spreading between patients. For example, in hospitals there is a strict policy of handwashing or using alcohol gel to clean hands before and after contact with each patient. All patients coming in for elective operations are screened for MRSA by taking swabs from the nostrils and all are asked to shower with an antibacterial shampoo and to use an antibacterial ointment in their nostrils for 3 days before admission. Patients who have previously had MRSA or who are identified as carriers on screening are isolated in individual rooms and tend to be put last on the operating list, so that the operating theatre can have a full clean after their operation. With these measures we have not had a new case of MRSA in 18 months.

Clostridium difficile is another hospital-associated infection which causes quite a different set of symptoms. Again, the bacteria can reside in the body (in the gut of 2-5% of the population) without causing symptoms. However, in patients whose normal gut bacterial flora is eradicated by our use of antibiotics the *C.difficile* can multiply to cause profuse diarrhoea and abdominal pains. In the elderly and debilitated especially this can progress to severe systemic illness with dilation and rupture of the colon if not appropriately treated. The disease is spread in hospitals, again, most commonly on the hands of healthcare professionals so, once again, a strict policy of handwashing and isolation of any affected patients can limit transmission. Avoidance of the use of certain antibiotics known to be particularly harmful to gut flora is also a positive preventative measure. Patients can usually be treated for *C.difficile* diarrhoea quite effectively with specific antibiotics (different to the ones that cause the problem in the first place)!

7.5   Swine Flu and Viral Pandemics

Like all organisms, bacterial and viral pathogens are constantly evolving from generation to generation to become more effective at invading the bodies of their hosts, evading the immune system, resisting our drugs and multiplying and spreading on to the next host. Likewise, our own immune systems must constantly adapt to these new strains of pathogen to control and eradicate infection. So, for example, each winter a new group of influenza viruses spreads through the population, lots of us get 'the flu' and our immune systems react to this slightly different flu bug and eventually rid our bodies of it. Then as these viruses spread through populations across the world they undergo small random mutations so that by the next winter they have changed just enough that they can give you the flu again before your immune system can wipe them out.

This relatively stable cycle can persist for years,but just occasionally a pathogen can undergo a change so radical that it catches our immune systems completely off guard and renders our vaccines and drugs entirely ineffective. This occurs particularly when a pathogen manages to cross the species barrier to a new host species and the influenza virus is a good example of this. There are variants of the influenza A virus that can infect waterfowl, chickens, pigs, whales and seals. Pigs are a particularly important host as they are susceptible both to human influenza viruses and avian influenza viruses. If, therefore, they are infected by an avian and a human influenza virus simultaneously, it is possible to get mixing of the genes of the viruses to produce an entirely new virus. This could potentially be one that transmits between humans but which has proteins on its surface to which the human immune system is entirely naive and thus gives us no immediate protection. In this way an influenza pandemic, which spreads to much of the world's population, could occur. The last truly disastrous pandemic was the so-called Spanish Flu pandemic of 1918-20 which killed 50 million people, but there have been more minor pandemics since. The 2009 Swine Flu pandemic was one of these and thankfully was far less significant in terms of mortality than first feared but still caused over 17,000 deaths worldwide. Though impossible to predict, it appears to be more of a case of when rather than if the next major pandemic will occur.

7.6 Vaccination against Cervical Cancer

Cervical cancer is the fifth leading cause of cancer death in women worldwide and in the UK is the second most common cancer diagnosed in women below the age of 35 years. It has been well known for some time that by far the most important risk factor for the development of cervical cancer is infection with certain sexually transmitted strains of the Human Papilloma Virus (other strains of this virus cause warts elsewhere on the body). In the developed world the implementation of regular testing with Pap smears has greatly reduced the incidence of death from cervical cancer as most cases are detected in the early non-invasive or pre-cancerous stages which are usually amenable to local treatments.

It still would be preferable, however, to reduce the chances of development of the abnormal cells in the first place, and two vaccines recently introduced onto the market appear to be able to do just this. The vaccines work by priming the immune system to fight off infection by the strains of HPV most closely linked to the development of cervical cancer and studies so far have shown that the protective effect will last at least 4.5 years from the time of vaccination and probably considerably longer.

In September 2008 the HPV vaccine was added to the UK national vaccination programme to be given to girls aged 12-13. This age was chosen as the vaccine has to be given before girls are exposed to the target strains of HPV to be effective - ie. before they become sexually active - but has sparked considerable controversy in the media. Various groups have opposed vaccination at this age on the basis that it will send an inappropriate message to pre-teens that it is acceptable or normal to become sexually active at that age. Another, perhaps more legitimate, concern is that unless there is careful education of the girls at the time of vaccination it may endow them with a false sense of invulnerability and make them more likely to engage in riskier sexual behaviour in the future. The HPV vaccine only targets the highest risk strains of HPV so there remains the possibility of developing cervical cancer if infected by other strains of the virus, and of course it gives no protection against all of the other sexually transmitted diseases that are out there. The message that has to be put across to the girls is that while the vaccine reduces the risks of cervical cancer, there can be no substitute for practicing safe sex.

7.7 The Right to Die and Assisted Suicide

The issues related to this topic have already been mentioned in our Interviews chapter. The issue has recently gained media attention when a number of celebrities including Sir Terry Pratchett publicly called on the government to open a debate into the introduction of assisted suicide in this country.

7.8 The NHS at 50: Where Do We Go From Here?

The National Health Service celebrated its 50th birthday in 2008 and remains one of the premier examples of universal, free at the point of contact healthcare in the world. The recent healthcare reforms in the USA and the debates that surrounded them have forced the concept of a nationalised health service into the spotlight with many questioning if we are really getting value for money compared to privatised healthcare in other countries (as we still pay for the NHS via our taxes). There is also the issue of what services should be available on the NHS and whether rationing of services will be necessary given the ever-increasing cost of healthcare and the limited NHS budget. Certainly a political hot potato and something you should try to have an opinion on. Again, this topic was touched on in the Interviews chapter.

Summary

There are numerous topics of potential interest to medical school interviewers and it is important, as a prospective medic, to be aware of them and be able to engage in informed discussion about them.

"You cannot teach a man anything; you can only help him find it within himself."

Galileo Galilei

Chapter 8

Oxbridge Applications

t is undeniable that Oxford and Cambridge Universities (often collectively termed 'Oxbridge') continue to hold a special place in the public's view of higher education in this country and around the world. It is for this reason that we have dedicated a chapter highlighting the different approach taken by Oxbridge to university education, including medical school. This is not to say that Oxbridge is better, but the way they structure themselves is usually different. Either way, whether it's Oxbridge or another medical school, it is important that you choose the university that is right for you. We hope this will help you in making that decision.

The Universities

Ah, Oxbridge. The dreaming spires, the boat race, eccentric academics, terrifying exams, garden parties with Pimms. It's almost impossible to have lived in this country for any length of time without having formed some kind of clichéd view of its most famous Universities.

While the academic gap between them and other Universities has closed, they continue to attract many of the brightest and best students thanks to the unique experience of studying in these legendary institutions, steeped in history. They offer the opportunity to be taught by world-leading experts in many fields, actively foster an interest in research during the course and offer many unique extra-curricular activities. This is all set against a beautiful backdrop of historic buildings in two towns which attract the interest of huge numbers of tourists. Indeed at times as a student here you will feel that you have become part of that tourist attraction. I'm fairly certain there are pictures of my graduation circulating right across North America and Asia!

Both universities offer six year undergraduate medicine courses, which include what is in essence an intercalated year in the third year of the course, plus a four year graduate entry course. They make no bones about the fact that during the application process they are looking primarily for the most academically gifted students, the thinkers, those who will go on to be 'the leaders of the medical profession'. Clearly all the other factors that go into being a good doctor are also taken into consideration, but the academic bias is more pronounced here than in other medical schools. Typical A-level offers have traditionally been AAA (including Chemistry plus at least one other science) but the 2010 introduction of an A* grade at A-level may push this even higher in coming years. In addition they will expect a high proportion of GCSE's at grades A* or A. For graduate entry applicants an upper second class honours degree would be a minimum requirement with equally good A-level results also preferable. The BMAT exam is required for undergraduate applicants to both Universities and at some colleges for the Cambridge graduate entry degree; the scores from this will significantly affect the success of your application. Likewise the UKCAT exam is used by the Oxford graduate entry course to directly compare academic abilities of applicants.

8.1 The College System

Both Oxford and Cambridge are collegiate universities, which means that in addition to applying to the university for their medical course, you will also apply to a specific college within the university and it will be academics from that college who will read your application, interview you and hopefully offer you a place. Your college then tends to form the core of your life at university for the first few years of the course, as it is the community in which you live, eat and socialise and it is also the college that provides academic support in the form of tutorials and pastoral support should you need it.

As each college only admits a small number of medical students each year you will find that the majority of the friends that you make within college are studying in other subject areas. This is a real bonus of the system as it prevents medics from becoming too insular early on in the course, while also giving you the opportunity to see how many arts students you can put off their dinner with stories of gross things you have seen in the anatomy labs! Each college also has a lively mix of extracurricular activities to keep you occupied when you are not studying, from sports teams (with regular inter-college competitions) to music and drama groups, to social events and the ever-important college bar. Whatever your interests, it should be possible to pursue them at the level you want, from laid back college bands meeting informally once a week, to the train-twice-a-day-until-it-takes-over-your-life-level University Blues Rowing teams that you see on the TV each year.

8.2 The Courses

Both undergraduate courses remain fairly traditional in their structure with formal lectures and lab sessions forming a large proportion of the teaching time in the first two years. These teaching sessions for the whole year group are supplemented by tutorials given in small groups (typically 2-4) arranged within your college several times each week. These 'tutes' are a longstanding Oxbridge tradition and provide an opportunity to explore topics in more depth while at the same time providing feedback on how you are doing and troubleshooting any problems that you may have.

The third year at both universities allows students to choose a specific subject to study in depth and perform a research project in. Both universities offer a range of preclinical science subjects to choose from but Cambridge also offers the possibility to spend a year doing less medical subjects such as philosophy, anthropology or law. Oxford offers one less scientific option, Philosophy, Psychology and Physiology (PPP), which takes an extra year to complete.

At the end of the third year of study students on both undergraduate courses are awarded a BA degree and have the option of either staying at the same university for the three years of clinical school (which about 50% opt for) or applying to move to either Imperial College, UCL or to the other colour of Oxbridge blue for clinical studies.

For those interested in a career in research and academic medicine the MB PhD program at Cambridge is worth a special mention. Places on this course will only be offered to the top graduates at the end of the three preclinical years. It essentially combines clinical school with a full PhD so takes 5 ½ to 6 years to complete, but would be an excellent way into an academic career.

8.3   Graduate Entry

The Cambridge graduate entry medicine course is unusual among grad entry courses in that students take the same core medical sciences course as the standard undergraduate course for the first 18 months, but additionally have clinical placements in hospitals and GP practices during the university vacations, which makes for a very busy schedule. The second half of the course follows a more standard series of clinical rotations as with other courses.

The Oxford graduate entry course, on the other hand, is more typical of the newer graduate courses in that the first year relies heavily on problem based learning rather than lectures, so learning is far more self-directed. Teaching from the second year of this course onwards is integrated in with the three clinical years of the standard undergraduate course right through to finals.

8.4 Applications

Applications for undergraduate and graduate entry medicine at Oxford and Cambridge must be submitted via UCAS by the 15th October for courses starting the following year. The graduate entry courses of both universities also require applicants to fill in an extra application form, which can be downloaded from their website, at the same time as the UCAS form. It should be remembered that school leavers applying for undergraduate courses cannot apply to both Oxford and Cambridge so you will need to choose. Applicants for the graduate entry courses are allowed to apply to both.

After receiving your UCAS application Cambridge University will e-mail you about another application form called the 'Supplementary Application Questionnaire' which must also be completed online (usually by the 22nd October so keep checking your e-mail about this – you don't want to miss it). This asks for things such as specific marks for A-level units which you have already sat (to more accurately compare results rather than relying just on predicted grades) and topics which you have covered on your A-level course (so that the interviewers know what areas you should know all about at interview).

As far as filling in the UCAS form goes there are no major differences relative to applying to other universities so our advice in the chapter earlier in this book still holds true. However, the option of choosing a specific college to apply for adds a whole extra level of complication to your decision making at this point. The first thing to consider is which colleges will actually take students for your chosen medical course. For example, if you were applying to Cambridge you could apply to any college except for Homerton and Hughes Hall for the six year medicine course but could only apply to Hughes Hall, Lucy Cavendish or Wolfson for the graduate entry course. To choose amongst the colleges there are a number of factors which you might wish to take into account:

1. Medical Student Quotas

Each year the University allocates a certain number of places for medicine to each of the colleges. There is a little flexibility within the system, but the number of first year medical students that each college admits tends to stay fairly constant from one year to the next and certain colleges take far more medics than others. This is of interest because you may prefer to choose a college with lots of medics in your year or alternatively to go somewhere where the tutors are focused on only a few of you. However, some applicants also try to use the admissions statistics which Cambridge publishes on their website each year (showing applicants and offers made for every subject at every college for the previous year) to try to pick the 'easiest' college to get into (i.e. the colleges with the fewest applicants per place). Unfortunately if you do this you may well find that other people have the same idea so the less popular colleges from last year may be more competitive this time around. Oxford prevents any of this type of subterfuge by refusing to publish precise admission statistics and by reallocating students among colleges before interviews if one college is particularly over or undersubscribed.

2. Academic League Tables

Each year Oxford University publishes the Norrington Table, which ranks all colleges by the grades achieved by their undergraduates in their final examinations. Cambridge has an equivalent table called the

Tompkins Table. One can use these as a crude guide to how focused a college is on academic achievements when assessing applicants, but remember that the standings in these league tables can vary quite a bit from year to year so look for trends over the past few years. Of course these rankings may also reflect differences in the quality of teaching between colleges.

3. Choose a place you will enjoy

As with choosing medical schools the most important consideration has to be choosing a college which you will enjoy living and studying in. Lots of things will play into this from location (at Pembroke College, Cambridge you can roll out of bed five minutes before lectures and still make it on time!) to accommodation (which varies from ultra modern to 14th Century) to clubs and to social life. Read through the prospectus to form a short list, but there really is no substitute for visiting and speaking to current students to find out what life is really like.

If you can't or do not want to decide on a college it is perfectly acceptable to send in an open application in which case the university will allocate you to a college that is not already overwhelmed with applicants.

8.5 The Interview

Oxford and Cambridge colleges tend to interview in December which is earlier than other medical schools. This means that if you are fortunate enough to be called for an interview it is likely to be the first 'real' one that you do so it is imperative that you have arranged a few mock interviews in the weeks leading up to it and had the chance to polish up your technique. There is a great deal of myth and mystique surrounding Oxbridge interviews and stories of rude, stuffy Dons asking bizarre and seemingly pointless questions abound. The reality is that these days an Oxbridge interview is likely to be quite similar to any other university interview with a series of questions that often start in areas you should be comfortable with (such as topics from your A-level syllabus or things you have seen on work experience) and then moving on to questions that will require more thought. They are not aiming to catch you out, instead they are looking for people who are able to work through problems and come up with reasoned arguments. Many interviews end up being like a miniature version of an Oxbridge college tutorial; the interviewers are essentially trying to find the candidates who will fit in well with the teaching system used in the university.

If, however, you do get a question that seems straight out of left field the first thing to say is don't panic! If you take a moment to think about the question it often becomes apparent after the initial shock that there is plenty for you to talk about, it is just the phrasing of the question that is unusual. For instance, a question such as "If you were a bacterium, what would you do?" might sound quite odd, but all it is really asking you to do is discuss the need to replicate, spread between hosts, evade the immune system, and so on. If, after a bit of thought, you still don't see what the interviewer is trying to get at it is perfectly acceptable to ask them to repeat or rephrase the question. Indeed it shows a certain amount of confidence to do so and is far better than sitting there without a clue!

We have given you a typical Oxbridge interview question for you to work through:

How might you measure the volume of blood in a live human being?

Speaking to our friends around us, this is actually quite a common question to be asked. The point of giving it to you here is not for you to memorise the answer just in case you get it too! Instead, it is to show you how you might think through an answer. Like many of the questions you will be asked, the underlying knowledge you need is fairly simple, based on GCSE chemistry. You may not immediately know the answer, or even where to begin. In the latter case, you may be steered by the interviewer to think about how one might usually measure volume. Try to really listen to what is being asked, clarify the question if you need, and do not become despondent if you feel you are not getting anywhere. You are meant to feel a bit like this!

Obviously, draining someone's blood into a measuring vessel will not do their body much good, so there needs to be another solution. Think about how you may measure volume in chemistry. We know that concentration is a measure of a known amount of substance in a known amount of liquid. If you were to manipulate this equation and add a known amount of a substance, allow it to freely disperse, and then measure its final concentration, you can then calculate the volume of liquid it must have been added to. "What are the potential problems with this method" I hear the interviewer asking? Well, think about it logically. The 'tracer' we are using has to be safe. We are assuming it disperses freely in the blood, and is not lost into tissues, or filtered through the kidneys before we have time to sample its concentration. Similarly, it must not be broken down in the blood stream. However, if we know how the tracer behaves in this manner we could alter our model to accommodate for this error.

You might be able to think of other answers to the questions, which are perfectly valid. This is just an example we have given. Questions often have multiple ways of tackling them and can have several solutions.

8.6 The Application Pool

Given the aforementioned occasional discrepancies between the number of applicants at each college and the number of places each actually has to offer, both Oxford and Cambridge run a pool system to redistribute good candidates more fairly between colleges. Oxford actually does this before the first round of interviews in December – it is possible that if you applied to a college that was particularly overwhelmed by applicants you may be invited to your first interview at an entirely different college which has not received as many applicants. This may seem a bit frustrating but it is done to give you a better chance of getting in so you can't really complain! At Cambridge your first interview will always be with the college you applied to.

After the first round of interviews in December colleges will give offers to the candidates they like best but often find that they have others who they feel are worthy of an offer but who they just don't have space to take. These applicants are then put forward into the 'pool' where colleges with spaces still left to fill review their applications and may well call them to interview. The pooling process takes place immediately after the first round of interviews in Oxford but is not until January in Cambridge. This means that after your interview you may be told sorry, we don't have space for you but we have put you forward into the pooled applications. This will obviously be disappointing at first but don't be disheartened, remember they have put you into the pool because they think you are good enough to deserve a place, there just doesn't happen to be one at that particular college. It does mean that you have to go through one or more extra interviews, but at least you will have a good chance of getting in somewhere so it's worth the extra few hours of stress!

Summary

The courses remain fairly traditional and the tutorial system offers a unique opportunity to explore topics in depth. The college system provides a focus for both work and play, even if it does complicate the application process slightly.

Remember that all the horror stories that you will have heard about Oxbridge interviews tend to be heavily embellished and exaggerated; they will almost certainly not be as unpleasant as you think they are going to be!

Chapter 9

Life as a Medical Student

So what is life like when you actually get to medical school? Many people are at least curious, if not a little worried about how life will be. As medics are such varied people, from such varied backgrounds, you are almost certainly going to find that there are many different lifestyles you can adopt. So, don't worry. You should fit in to the tapestry somewhere. We can give you some general pointers based on our own experiences, and those of others around us, but ultimately your own time at medical school is going to be different to others around you.

9.1 A Lengthy Course

The first obvious thing about being a medical student is that you are in for the long haul, usually five or six years. Most other courses at university are three years, occasionally four. This means your peers doing other subjects are likely to disappear half way through your course. The offshoot of this is that many medics integrate with other students in the preclinical years, and then become more 'medic-y' in the clinical years. Of course, many people keep in touch with old friends from other subjects, or make new friends, but it is certainly true that the year group of medics become closer in the latter years of the course. This is really nice, sort of like a big family, and people are usually very supportive of one another. Quite often you will find groups of students studying together in the library, testing one another and preparing for exams.

9.2   A Typical Day as a Medical Student

Many prospective medical students wonder what their typical day may be like during their time at university. One of the best things about studying medicine is that pretty much every day is different. Whilst you may be in the same place most days, you will be introduced to lots of new concepts, ideas and patients to keep you on your toes. Depending on how the course is structured, you may have a mixture of formal lectures with lab work and teaching in a clinical setting or a clearer split with more lectures in the early years and more time on the wards in the latter years. Generally, as is common to most 'science' students, you will have teaching scheduled at 9am, so you will not be able to lie in every morning as some 'arts' students do. You should expect most of the day to be taken up by scheduled teaching or with work set such as a lab write-up or an essay. Weekends are invariably free, but many students find themselves studying if they have an approaching exam or essay set. Having said this, most people will have time to pursue their hobbies and interests in the time around formal teaching. In fact, students often shoot off for a game of football or orchestra in the time between scheduled teaching.

9.3   Freshers' Week

'Freshers' Week' is the first one or two (some universities like to extend the fun) weeks at university. It is a time dedicated to helping new students to make friends and settle in. You will not have formal teaching in this time and so your days will be quite different when you first start your course. Freshers' Week is usually run by a mixture of older students, who organise activities during the days and evenings of your first weeks at medical school. There is often a special 'medical' branch for medical students, on top of the university scheme. Freshers' Week has a reputation for being a pretty raucous start to adult education, and it certainly can be this, but there are always a broad number of activities organised to reach out beyond the fancy dress and nightclub scene. It's a good way of getting out of your room and introducing yourself to your future friends, so get stuck in and make the most of it. Soon enough, you will have those 9am lectures to attend!

9.4 Accommodation

As a general rule, the majority of first year medical students live in 'halls of residence.' These usually take the form of a collection of flats or houses that are grouped together. They often have a group of older students that organise special social events. Each hall will vary, some having en-suite bathrooms and others not, some being self catered and others catered. Some halls are in the centre of town or close to the university, others are a bit further out. This isn't always a bad thing as it can encourage a strong group atmosphere, and these halls are often some of the most fun to live in. Universities will outline their halls of residence in their prospectus, and you will have to apply to them in advance. The vast majority of those who get in to their first choice course will gain their first, second or third choice halls. However, if you go to your back-up choice, or gain a place via clearing, you may find you have to be flexible in your choice of accommodation. Some universities use a collegiate system, in which first years will live within the college. Check out the 'Oxbridge' section for more information on this.

Although some students are offered the opportunity to stay in halls, most people 'live out' in subsequent years. This usually involves getting together with a few mates and finding somewhere to rent together. You have to deal with paying bills and communal cleaning, but it is great fun to live in a 'proper' house with your friends. Mature or graduate students are more likely to choose to live out from their first year, perhaps living with a partner. Some universities also offer accommodation for married couples.

Of course, some of you will be considering staying at home and commuting into medical school. People have a variety of reasons for this, ranging from family illness to low funds. Sometimes it is absolutely the right thing to do, but if you are thinking of living at home because you are worried about leaving home or having independence then we would encourage you to take the plunge and try living in halls. It is a great way of meeting people, studying with others on your course, and essentially taking steps to be a grown up! You can request to live in a single sex flat if you wish. We aren't saying you have to move to the other side of the country, but you can always use your weekends to visit home if you are worried about leaving your family and home friends. Take a look at the 'Finance' chapter for information on funding your accommodation rent.

9.5 Student Societies

Medical schools usually have fantastic, specialised societies for their students. These are available to you throughout your time at university but, again, tend to really come in to the fore in the latter years. There will usually be at least one common room, or maybe a whole building on the hospital site for clinical students to chill out and work in. Events are organised to cater for all sorts of tastes, from pantomimes, to nights out, to coffee mornings and free lunches. You may have to pay a small joining fee, but people in financial hardship are usually helped out. The medic society will be on top of what the university has to offer you so you will have lots to keep you busy.

9.6 Student Support

Both the medical school and the university will be able to offer you pastoral support if you need it. Many students find stress can get on top of them, or they miss home, and if this happens to you don't be afraid to ask for help. It is really common and there are loads of people you can talk to in confidence. Seeing sick patients every day can wear you down and it is important to take time to recharge your batteries. Otherwise things can build up and you may not be able to cope very well. Likewise, keep an eye on your friends around you to make sure they are okay. We have found that some people at medical school can be a bit too competitive and end up isolating themselves. Try to remember that everyone can do well and that sharing any tips or experiences in order to help others will come back in the other direction in some form or another. Some people learn this lesson a bit late and miss out on some great friendships.

9.7 Each School is Unique

Each medical school has a slightly different 'flavour' that will affect your time there. Some people find it useful to sample this before they apply by going on an open day or speaking to a current student. For example, the lifestyle in a big city such as London may be different to that in smaller cities or towns. You may want to be near lots of nightclubs or prefer to be close to the countryside so that you can go horse-riding in your spare time. Some people may choose a university because of its prestige in a certain sport. As we have mentioned, lots of different people go to medical school, and you are very likely to find people that you will get on with. If your medical school does not have a particular society that you had wished to be involved with then why not set up your own one?

All this opportunity for fun requires quite a lot of organisation so that you don't fall behind with work. As you can see from Georgie's profile it is certainly possible to do well at medical school, compete to a high level in sport, and still have time to see your friends and enjoy yourself. If you have aspirations such as this then you will need to plan ahead. Get your essays in on time and do not fall behind. Having lots of extracurricular activities will look really impressive when you apply for jobs because it shows you are well organised. Do not feel that you have to fill up every hour of the day with activities though. It's perfectly fine to have time to yourself with a cup of tea and a film! Try not to worry too much about fitting in at medical school. If you are accepted to study to be a doctor then it is clear that you are likely to have some social skills and there are bound to be others around you that you will get on with. Some people hit it off as they move into their student digs on the first day, whilst others take a week or two to find people with similar interests. Remember that everyone will be in the same boat and nervous on that first day. Just take a deep breath and give people a friendly smile. This worked for us, anyway! In the end, the whole year will come together and you may make friends that not only have vastly different interests and backgrounds to you, but friends that you will keep in touch with for the rest of your life.

Summary

The vast majority of medics settle into and enjoy medical school. Most students live in 'halls' for their first year, and then 'live out.' The course often takes up much of the day, but you will have spare time to enjoy yourself! There is a plethora of activities to get involved in, to suit all interests.

Profile: Georgina Baines
BA

Georgie is a 6th year medical student at Oxford University and has already completed a BA in Genetics and Development. Her main academic interests include the molecular science of medicine, especially genetics. Clinically, Georgie has contributed to a study on Sudden Cardiac Death, which has been published and subsequently presented at conference. She is also involved in a study looking at the effect of ketones on the performance of elite athletes. Georgie plans to pursue a career in surgery although hasn't ruled out other options at this stage. Away from medicine Georgie loves rowing, having been a member of the Oxford University boat for over four years and has raced at both Henley and the European University Championships. Other interests include sailing, eating and partying!

Georgie's Story

"I'm Georgie Baines. I'm a sixth year medic at Merton College, Oxford. I've pretty much always wanted to do medicine! At school I loved the sciences, but thought that studying one of them at university might be a bit dry and not very broad. I picked medicine because I found the workings of the body fascinating, and thought a career as a doctor would be much better than an office or lab job. Since coming to medical school, I have found it an incredibly varied experience, which I have enjoyed much more than I thought I would! There are so many different areas to learn about, you never get bored. As a medical student, you have to pick up a lot of different skills as well as facts, so

146

it's not all bookwork. I haven't decided yet what I would like to go into, but medicine is such a broad subject that I'm sure I will find a speciality which will suit me.

I row for the University Lightweight Women's squad and have done since my second year. I find that it is really good to have an interest outside of medicine. The subject can get pretty full on at times, and it is nice to have a break to refresh yourself! For rowing, we train twice a day, once in the morning, once in the evening and all through the morning at weekends. At first it was quite tough to fit this in with medicine. However as the years have gone by I have got used to going straight from the gym to the hospital, then back to the gym. It also makes me appreciate Fridays (my day off training) a lot! This training commitment means I have to be super organised, which I think feeds into my work. If you don't have a lot of free time, you just have to do work as soon as you can, which means I hardly ever have 'essay crises.' It's not all easy though - sometimes I do have to make excuses and leave the hospital early but on the whole the doctors are understanding. I have also had to do my training on my own when a tutorial couldn't be rescheduled, which can be tough when the rest of the boat have done it together. It's definitely tough, but it's worth it for that feeling of achievement at the end of the year when I've done the Boat Race and, (fingers crossed!) passed my exams. With all this commitment I have invariably had to cut down my social life a bit, though this just means when I do go out I make it count!

In general, the advice I would give to people thinking of doing medicine is go for it! It's a long course, but incredibly interesting and varied. Medicine is perfect for well balanced individuals who are interested in science and fancy a job doing something rewarding and intellectually challenging. It's also good if, like me, you don't entirely know what you want to do, as there are so many options open to you from lab-based jobs to community work. For the application process, I would advise you to get as much work experience as possible. This will give you an idea of whether medicine really is the career for you, and will also look really good on your UCAS form. Reading scientific magazines like 'New Scientist' is also useful in cultivating an inquisitive mind, and will help you out in interviews.

Best of luck!"

"My doctor gave me six months to live, but when I couldn't pay the bill he gave me six months more."

Dick Wilson

Chapter 10

Finances

Studying to become a doctor comes at a price. Literally. Gone are the days of the classic student grant, with these being replaced by tuition and top-up fees as well as the requirement to pay one's own 'living' costs. The good news is that there is a comprehensive scheme to loan money to UK residents to cover fees and living costs. This is called a student loan. If you are a student from the EU you can also apply for a loan to cover your fees, but not for living costs. This money does not start to be paid back until you are earning a certain amount. At the time of print this threshold is £15,000 per year and you pay the loan back at a rate of 9% on any earnings above this.

Many of us worry about accumulating debt. It's not a great feeling to know that you owe thousands of pounds to the government. However, a good piece of news to temper this worry is that the total amount of money you have to pay back is much lower than with commercial loans, and is subsidised by the government. The rate of interest that you pay on the loan is set each year. In fact, the levels of interest set for September 2009 to August 2010 is zero%, meaning the amount of money you owe in this time does not accumulate. In previous years, the rate has been a little higher, around the level of inflation, for example at 3.8% in September to December 2008. Because of the effect of inflation, this has meant that the value of the loan does not increase in real terms. Check out the government's information at *www.direct.gov.uk*, following links to student finance or *www.studentloanrepayment.co.uk* if you would like to know more.

If you stop earning above £15,000 per year for whatever reason, you stop paying back the loan until you get above the threshold again. If you travel overseas for more than three months, you must inform the Student Loans Company. You have to send evidence of your earnings, and continue to pay the relevant amount of money as you would do in the UK.

So, the killer question: how much debt will I have when I qualify? This varies massively from individual to individual, not just in the assistance they may receive from parents, but also in terms of how prudent they are in managing their money. The British Medical Association (BMA) undertakes a survey of final year medical students every year to ask them about their debt. The average level for 2008/09 was £22,871. Obviously there was a range either side of this. The BMA publish their results each year online at *www.bma.org.uk*.

10.1   Putting the Loan into Perspective

As we have mentioned earlier in the book, doctors get paid a reasonable starting salary, which notches up fairly well as you move up the ranks. Of course, having 9% of what you earn over £15,000 per year taken out of your salary is not going to fill you with joy, but it should be manageable. *It should not put you off applying for medicine!* There are a number of ways in which students from low income backgrounds are given help. In addition, all students are entitled to support from the NHS in their final two years. These schemes will be covered in this chapter. The bulk of the information in the 'Sources of Funding' section applies to students living in England at the time of print, but has many points in common with Scottish and Welsh systems. There is a brief introduction to the Scottish and Welsh systems below, that you can supplement with the websites we have recommended if required.

Scottish residents studying medicine at a Scottish university will have their tuition fees paid for by the government, although you have to fill out a yearly form to facilitate this. If you are a Scot studying outside Scotland, you will have to pay fees, but can get a loan to cover this, as English students do. Students from outside Scotland but studying in Scotland pay fees. The Scottish system has a student loan scheme to cover living costs, and is assessed on a similar means-tested (parental income) basis to the English system. There are also bursaries called the 'Young Students' and 'Independent Students' bursaries, which are worth up to £2,640 and £1,000 respectively, depending on your parental income. They replace part of the student loan, meaning there is less money to pay back for students that qualify. The website for more information on Scottish funding can be found at ***www.student-support-saas.gov.uk***.

Welsh residents also have a different system to navigate. Again, there is a student loan scheme available. The 'Assembly Learning Grant' is a grant worth up to £5,000 that is assessed based on parental income. At the time of print, the first £2,844 of money awarded is substituted from the maintenance part of the student loan. This means it reduces the amount of loan, and hence the amount repayable. The 'Special Support Grant' offers the same level of funding, but is aimed to help lone parents or those with a student partner and also for students with disabilities. The Welsh system also has a 'Welsh Bursary Scheme', which is a means tested grant given to both Welsh residents and UK residents studying in Wales.

10.2 Sources of Funding

As you will see from this chapter, there are lots of different sources of money to help support you through your studies. You will need to be *organised* in thinking about what you want to apply for and then apply well in advance. There can be quite a lot of paperwork involved and you will need to provide evidence to prove your details. Have a sit down, perhaps with your parents, to discuss your options and prepare a budget of your expected expenses and income. This will enable you to see at a glance what your funding requirements are likely to be. Getting used to preparing and sticking to budgets before university is a great idea and we will provide you with some advice on budgeting later in the chapter.

One thing to bear in mind about the money that you can apply for in the form of a loan or a grant is that the amount you receive is 'income assessed'. Everyone is entitled to a certain minimum but any extra depends on what your parents earn and what savings they hold. This is, in our opinion, not an ideal system as it involves the underlying assumption that parents earning over a certain amount are likely to be able to support their children financially. Sometimes this is not the case and you may need to find alternate sources of funding, a few of which we will mention in this chapter. There are separate conditions for people who do not have parents or who are estranged from them, or who have been living independently for a certain amount of time. Check out the 'student finance calculator' function on the student finance section of ***www.direct.gov.uk*** to get an idea of where you stand.

Sources of Loans and Funding

1. Student Loan

This is divided up into two sections. You are entitled to receive a student loan to cover your course *tuition fees* in full. At the time of print this is a maximum of £3,225 per year. You are also entitled to a student loan for *maintenance,* which is worth up to £4,950 per year and is intended to help with covering living expenses. You will get more maintenance if you are living in London to account for the overall higher cost of living in the capital.

2. Government grants

This is called a *'Maintenance'* or *'Special Support'* grant. It is a source of money that is allocated based upon parental income. It is worth up to £2,906 per year, and should help you cope with living costs, although the amount of money you get from the maintenance student loan may be reduced if you apply successfully for these grants. The great news is this grant does not have to be paid back!

3. University Bursaries

If you are entitled to a full maintenance or special support grant then universities are required to offer you some extra bursary. The actual amount varies between universities but for the 2009/2010 intake the typical bursary offered for institutions charging full tuition fees was £800. Again, this money does not need to ever be paid back and should go some way to making students from low income backgrounds more comfortable.

4. Hardship Funds

There is additional help available for students who still have a gap in their income because of extenuating circumstances. This is in the form of the *Access to Learning Fund.* Examples include a parent losing their job, having to make essential household repairs or not receiving help from parents despite them being assessed at a certain income level. It does not account for reckless spending, and you have to give bank statements to explain your spending. In theory, you may apply for this fund every year of your studies. The amount of money awarded is typically in the hundreds range, although it is not unheard of to be awarded much more. It will depend on individual circumstances. The website ***www.direct.gov.uk*** has a section on Access to Learning. Follow the links via 'getting extra help'.

Scotland has a similar fund called 'Discretionary Funds' and Wales a 'Financial Contingency Fund'. They work in a very similar way to the Access to Learning Fund.

5. NHS Bursary

You can apply for this scheme if you are doing a standard five or six year medical course and it covers your penultimate two years. You are entitled to the full amount of your tuition fees to be paid by the NHS direct to your university. You will receive around half the rate of student maintenance loan but receive extra money to cover this shortfall in the form of a grant from the NHS. Unfortunately this latter money is assessed on parental income and occasionally people find themselves with half the maintenance loan they are used to, with no NHS top-up. This is rare and should be made up from other sources, such as Access to Learning.

Graduate students are also entitled to NHS support. For a four year course, graduates receive help in their second, third and final years. Students may also be eligible for other funding in their first year. This means that studying medicine as a graduate student is less pricey than many people expect. Good news we think!

6. Other Help for Medics

As a medical student you should be prepared to do a fair amount of travelling, especially in your clinical years. You may be sent out to a district general hospital to complete a rotation, or have to commute daily to a placement in general practice. The government has a scheme to pay essential travel expenses for medical students, but you currently must cover the first £303 yourself. However, many medical schools are reasonable in refunding travel expenses that are incurred as part of their course. Usually you would be asked to provide a receipt and your bank details, and the money fairy then magically delivers your expenses into your account! Simple. Some medical schools have special scholarships or bursaries that you can apply to for assistance. They want you to focus on your studies, rather than money problems and therefore are usually very helpful.

7. Help for Disabled Students

Students with an impairment, health condition or learning difficulty such as dyslexia may be entitled to additional financial help. Health conditions include mental health problems. The money is aimed at levelling the field so that everyone has an equal chance of studying medicine and being successful in their course.

10.3 Other Sources of Money

1. Personal Savings

Some students are lucky or prudent enough to accumulate some money before setting off for university. This may have been earned on a gap year, saved over a period of time or perhaps an inheritance, to name but a few potential sources. Bear in mind that you will have to declare any savings when applying for loans and grants and the amount saved may affect the amount of money you are then entitled to.

2. Parental Contributions

Many students are fortunate enough to get partially or fully funded through university by their parents or other relatives. Others may take a 'loan' from their parents, which they pay back later in life, hopefully at low interest!

3. Overdrafts

There are some fantastic student accounts about with interest free overdrafts and some great introductory offers as well. Usually the interest-free time extends into life as a graduate, giving you time to pay off the overdraft before you have to pay interest on it. When selecting a bank account be aware that features such as the size of available overdraft (ideally interest free) with a local bank you trust may be more important than a free MP3 player in the long term!

4. Employment & Entrepreneurship

Some medics manage to make some extra money by getting a part time job. Remember that you will be on a demanding course and that it should take priority. Your course may mean you have to work unusual or unpredictable hours that make working a regular part-time job more difficult compared with other students. Having said that, some medics get paid great money for doing the odd bit of tutoring, or a more flexible job. Others work during the longer holidays at the beginning of the course.

The entrepreneurs amongst you may decide to use your talents to set up a means of getting some extra cash, such as forming a band to play at local functions. Have a word with your course tutor for advice before committing yourself to something you may not be able to fulfil.

10.4 Budgeting

It is easy to let money issues run away with you if you are not organised about how you manage your finances. We have put together some top tips that we have learnt along the way so you can keep some of that much needed cash for things you really want and need!

1. Know Where You Stand

Ignorance is bliss, right? Well, not when you realise you only have 50p to your name. It happens! Check your bank statements regularly and be aware of what money is coming into your account and what is being spent, including regular expenses such as rent and utility bills. Internet banking is a fantastic tool to find out immediately what is going in and out. If you know well in advance that there is going to be a funding gap you can apply to the relevant funds to fill it, before times get really tough.

2. Books and Equipment

Let's start with the obvious. Libraries exist and are full of useful books! There is often no need to go and buy every item on a reading list. This is especially the case at times when you may need a particular book for only a few months of your course. If you really do feel the need to buy books, such as some of the more 'essential' textbooks, then why not consider hunting down those second-hand deals that exist, rather than forking out huge amounts for brand new books. They may be sold at a second hand bookshop, online, or from a friend in a year above. A lot of student societies run second-hand book sales at the start of term so keep an eye on the notice board.

These days much of our learning as medical students comes from papers from scientific journals. These can usually be accessed online using university subscriptions, often from home using a relevant login. This is a great way of getting really cutting edge information for free. Check out websites such as ***www.ncbi.nlm.nih.gov/pubmed/*** for original research and useful summaries of specific topics. Talk to your university library about how to access journals and other resources. In fact, befriending the medical library staff early on during your time at university is a great idea!

3. Lifestyle Changes

Some of us get into bad habits whilst living at home with parents. Are you used to the fridge always being full, or being dropped off by your parents in the car each day? If so, try shopping for food that you will actually eat, and do not eat out every day in cafes and restaurants. Buy a cheap bike to cycle about town instead of having to pay insurance and tax on a car, or unnecessary bus fares. Smoke? Well, why not quit? Seriously, try. You will save loads of money and improve your health at the same time. Simple measures such as setting yourself a weekly budget can help you get on top of your finances and free up money for what you really want to spend your cash on. For larger expenses such as balls and holidays, you may have to make some sacrifices and go on one rather than both. Tough thing to do, but that's life.

4. Bargain Hunting

Unfortunately we cannot all rely on trust funds to support lavish lifestyles and most of us need to seek out the odd bargain or two in order to keep solvent. For those who know where to look there are loads of really great, genuine, bargains to be had from deals on food at your favourite cafes and restaurants, to getting your hair cut the way you want. There are some great 'buy one, get one free' offers and the like out there for students. Check out websites such as **www.studentbeans.com** for vouchers, offers and competitions to save you some cash when treating yourself! We could write a whole separate book on bargain hunting for students and a lot of the lessons will be learnt once you're actually at university.

10.5 More information

The website **www.money4medstudents.org** is a really fantastic site that gives information on all the funding available throughout the UK as well as extra private funds you can apply to. It has a 'budget planner' function and top tips on reducing expenditure. It really deserves a special mention and we recommend you and your parents check it out.

Summary

Studying medicine will cost a significant amount of money, with the main expenses being tuition fees and living costs. There is a student loan scheme to help students cover the cost of both components.

There are, in addition, many extra schemes designed to assist those from low and middle-income backgrounds.

Managing your money sensibly is essential if you are to keep your debt as low as possible. Keep track of your income and expenditure from day one.

Chapter 11

Career options

For those of you that see this title and say "well duh, I want to be a doctor obviously" this chapter is for you above all others. A medical degree opens the door to a huge range of career options both within the confines of the NHS career ladder and elsewhere. There is no such thing as a generic doctor these days. Everybody specialises to a degree and there is encouragement to do so earlier and earlier after graduation. It's worth thinking about this during your time at medical school as you can usefully tailor things like your electives towards potential careers and more importantly if you can get a job in the foundation years in your area of interest then, not only is it more enjoyable, but it will also look good when you apply for specialist training. Some students have an idea of which area of the medical profession they would like to end up in before they even start at medical school and, if that applies to you, that's great and is worth mentioning in your personal statement and at interview since it shows that you have been thinking ahead. Do bear in mind however that most people's ideas change over the course of their degree and their first few years in practice when they are actually exposed to the realities of the job.

11.1   The Foundation Programme

This was introduced in 2005 and replaced the old Pre-registration House Officer and Senior House Officer years with a two year structured programme that acts as a bridge between medical school and specialty training. During these two years trainees rotate through a series of jobs lasting 3 to 6 months with the aim of being exposed to a number of different specialties while gaining competence in basic clinical and patient-management skills. There is a mandatory structured teaching programme and a number of assessments, which must be performed before trainees are allowed to complete foundation training. The first foundation year must be completed before doctors are allowed to become fully registered as medical practitioners with the General Medical Council (GMC).

If they are planning to continue to work within the NHS then during the winter of the second foundation year (FY2) trainees apply to training posts in the specialty in which they wish to work. This is a fairly crucial decision as it will likely determine the course of the rest of their careers, though there is always some opportunity to change training schemes later on. Depending on the specialty, training can take up to a further 10 years before doctors are at Consultant level, with a whole series of courses and exams to pass along the way to become a member of the Royal College for the relevant specialty.

11.2 Careers Within The NHS

Hospital Medicine

Hospital Medicine encompasses a huge range of 30 different specialties from Infectious Diseases to Cardiology to Sports Medicine, treating most of the conditions for which patients are admitted to hospital. Most specialties focus on specific body systems, but there is always a need for general medics and geratologists (physicians who specialize in care of elderly patients) to take a broader view of patients. These are some of the jobs where the most detective work is needed, with a combination of clinical skills, lab tests and imaging being needed to reach diagnoses. The training pathway involves two years of Core Medical training after the foundation years to gain a range of experience before applying again for more specialist training to run through to consultant level.

See **www.rcplondon.ac.uk** for further sources of information.

Surgical Careers

Surgical jobs tend to be amongst the most competitive to get in to of all possible medical careers, and amongst the most demanding in terms of on-call commitments outside of normal working hours right up to and including consultant level. The payback for all this work is a job full of interesting technical challenges using fancy bits of kit and the satisfaction of producing immediate results for your patients in the operating theatre. There is also the opportunity for consultants to earn a significant amount of money doing private work in addition to NHS commitments.

There are nine main surgical specialties, with many smaller subspecialties within these:

1. **General Surgery** – The largest specialty, encompasses surgery of the bowels, blood vessels, breast and endocrine glands, plus transplant surgery.

2. **Cardiothoracic Surgery** – Operate on the organs of the chest. These tend to be major operations on patients who may be medically quite unwell.

3. **Urology** – These surgeons deal with conditions of the kidneys and bladder, plus conditions of the male reproductive system.

4. **ENT (Ear, Nose and Throat)** – Deal with a variety of diseases in the head and neck, do little emergency work and treat most of their patients as day-cases.

5. **Maxillofacial** – Requiring both medical and dental degrees, surgeons in this specialty operate on conditions of the facial bones, mouth and neck.

6. **Neurosurgery** – Surgery of the brain and spinal cord, stressful with a lot of cases coming in as emergencies.

7. **Orthopaedics** – Often unfairly mocked as the carpenters of the medical world, they work on bones, joints and soft tissues (and yes, they use a variety of powertools!).

8. **Paediatric surgery** – A small specialty providing surgical treatment for many diseases and malformations of childhood, hence operate on various areas of the body.

9. **Plastic surgery** – Not just boob jobs! A very varied specialty and very competitive to get into, includes work with burns, hand surgery and soft tissue injury to the face, torso and limbs.

After foundation training, aspiring surgeons will do two years of Core Surgical training in which they will work in a number of surgical specialties to gain a broad variety of skills. They must then go through a second competitive application process to get onto a training scheme lasting approximately six years in their chosen specific surgical specialty.

See *www.rcseng.ac.uk* for further sources of information.

Other Hospital Specialties

There are quite a few specialties within a hospital which are distinct from the departments of Medicine and Surgery. Each has its own training programme.

165

1. Emergency Medicine

A challenging career where doctors see a high throughput of very varied patients and have to become experts in rapidly assessing and stabilising patients - certainly this job will never be dull! Hospitals need to provide an emergency service 24 hours a day, 365 days a year so doctors work a considerable number of unsociable shifts which will put some off this career.

See *www.collemergencymed.ac.uk* for further sources of information.

2. Radiology

A specialty which is evolving rapidly beyond its original remit of using X-rays and other imaging techniques to help to diagnose disease. As technology improves there is now the scope to perform minimally invasive procedures under the guidance of ultrasound or CT scanning to treat conditions where previously a major operation would have been required. Of course there still is a fair amount of time spent sitting in a darkened room looking at pictures of peoples insides!

See *www.rcr.ac.uk* for further sources of information.

3. Obstetrics and Gynaecology

A wide-ranging career covering all aspects of the care of the pregnant woman and the unborn child, plus treatment of diseases of the female reproductive system. Most consultants develop a particular interest or subspecialty in one particular area. The specialty offers a combination of medical and surgical problems which makes for a varied workload.

See *www.rcog.org.uk* for further sources of information.

4. Paediatrics

This is a career that interests a lot of medical students when they are exposed to it during their studies. Caring for children is hugely rewarding and paediatrics is one of the few specialties where it is still possible to be a generalist due to the variety of conditions seen. It requires good diagnostic skills as children frequently present with very non-specific symptoms and may be unable to communicate what is wrong. It does, however, require a degree of mental fortitude as caring for seriously ill and dying children can be very difficult.

See *www.rcpch.ac.uk* for further sources of information.

5. Psychiatry

Dealing with all aspects of mental health, psychiatry demands excellent interpersonal and clinical skills as there is very little help from technology for making a diagnosis. As treatments have improved many more patients can be treated in their own homes rather than being admitted to hospital.

See *www.rcpsych.ac.uk* for further sources of information.

6. Anaesthetics

Anaesthetists are vital members of the surgical team with their increasingly advanced techniques allowing surgeons to perform ever more complex operations. There is far more to the career than that however, with their excellent knowledge of airway management and physiology making them vitally important in emergency situations and in the intensive care setting.

See *www.rcoa.ac.uk* for further sources of information.

7. Pathology

With less patient contact than other specialties, pathologists instead use a variety of laboratory-based tests to assist the other specialties in making early and accurate diagnosis of diseases.

See ***www.rcpath.org*** for further sources of information.

General Practice

Although considered a less glamorous career by many medical students, the more junior doctors are exposed to General Practice the more attractive it becomes. The key attraction is the variety of work, pleasant working environment and the long-term relationships that can be built up with patients. It also offers a shorter training scheme and a far more acceptable work-life balance than any of the hospital specialties as currently GP's can choose if they wish to do any work at evenings and weekends.

GP specialty training is currently entered directly from foundation year 2 and is a 3 year training scheme where trainees spend part of the time in various hospital specialties and part in a general practice. There are currently plans to increase the length of the training scheme to 5 years in coming years.

See ***www.rcgp.org.uk*** for further sources of information.

Public Health Medicine

These physicians deal with the health need of whole communities rather than individuals. Their job involves the monitoring of communicable diseases and environmental health, the provision of information and education, plus providing support to primary care trusts to improve services.

See *www.fph.org.uk* for further sources of information.

Research Careers

There has always been a strong focus on research in medicine and this is being further encouraged by the invention of academic jobs within the NHS at foundation training level and above. These jobs combine periods of clinical practice with periods of research and are a perfect stepping stone to further research either within the NHS or within the Biomedical industry. There is also the possibility of going into academia, working in a university setting, combining conducting research with teaching students.

11.3   Careers Outside of The NHS

Although the majority of applicants to medical school are planning to work in the NHS that is by no means the only option available to medical graduates.

Biomedical Industry

There is always a call for doctors to supervise and run clinical trials and to monitor drug safety within the pharmaceutical industry. Although patient contact may be minimal there is still a call for good communication skills as you will be interacting with employees from a range of backgrounds from biochemistry to marketing.

Military Careers

Each branch of the armed forces has its own medical service to which they recruit medical students and qualified doctors. They offer bursaries and cadetships to students as they go through medical school, which provide generous funding as long as you are willing to sign up for an agreed number of years after graduation. The training opportunities are fairly unique but clearly if you are planning to return to civilian medicine after your years of service there are certain career paths that the military would not be suited to. For example, there is not much of a call for paediatricians in the Royal Marines for example!

Forensic Medical Examiners

These doctors are for the most part general practitioners who work with the police force on a part-time basis. Much of their work involves examining individuals detained by the police though they may occasionally be called to crime scenes. They are often called upon to provide evidence in court so must be prepared to deal with that type of adversarial situation.

Prison Medicine

Again these are usually trained general practitioners who provide medical services to inmates in the countries' prisons. Treatments that can be prescribed to inmates are somewhat restricted for fear of drug abuse so consultations can feel confrontational if not carefully managed.

Travel

Medicine is a career which travels like no other. Wherever there are people there will be people getting sick so there will be a job for you. You may need to sit further exams to be able to practice in certain countries such as the USA, but for many, such as Australia and New Zealand, your UK qualifications are sufficient on their own. The possibilities are endless, from 'First World' medicine in the aforementioned countries to humanitarian work with organisations such as Médecins Sans Frontières. It is therefore possible to travel the world and continue a fascinating career at the same time.

Alternative Careers

If you are looking for a complete change, medical degrees are widely respected by employers and equip graduates with skills that are readily transferrable to other careers. So if you go through all of your training and decide that medicine just isn't for you then there is a whole world of other graduate jobs out there, from banking to management consultancy.

Summary

The process of becoming a doctor may appear daunting in terms of the competition to get into medical school, the long term commitment to learning and hard work and the financial costs of the course. However, the reward is an enormous variety of career opportunities after graduation which means that there is bound to be a rewarding and enjoyable job somewhere in the world for you that makes it all worthwhile.

Profile: Surgeon Lieutenant Adam Hewitt Smith RN

Adam graduated from Imperial College, London in 2006 with a medical degree and intercalated science degree (MBBS BSc) and, after completing his foundation years in the NHS, started working full time as a Medical Officer in the Royal Navy. He currently works as the Medical Officer to 45 Commando Royal Marines at RM Condor, Arbroath in both primary and pre-hospital care. Adam is due to enter specialty training in 2012 and plans to become a consultant in emergency and pre-hospital medicine.

Adam's Story

"I had read about working as a doctor in the Armed Forces while studying for my A Levels at school. The opportunity to practice medicine in some of the most wide-ranging and challenging environments in the world immediately drew my attention. After contacting the local Armed Forces Careers Office for more information, I let things go quiet until my third year of medical school. The Royal Navy, Army and Royal Air Force all offer medical cadetships that provide students with significant financial support, but only during the last three years of medical school. I applied for a cadetship from the Royal Navy and having passed the Admiralty Interview Board (a series of exams, leadership tests and interviews) I became a Medical Officer. During my last three years at medical school I was left pretty much alone to concentrate on studying and passing my exams. I was encouraged to join the local University Royal Naval Unit but was unable to, because of musical and sporting commitments. In 2006 I qualified as a doctor from Imperial College, London and moved to Oxford. I completed my Foundation Years 1 and 2 in Oxford and High Wycombe, working in general medicine, general surgery, accident and emergency and paediatrics.

In return for sponsorship during medical school and your foundation years, the Royal Navy ask for a return of service of six years from full registration with the General Medical Council. In actual fact, three of these years are spent in the NHS training like your civilian colleagues and only three are spent working full time as a junior doctor in the Royal Navy. This is your chance to practice medicine in places and situations most people can only dream of and it will probably be the most rewarding part of your military career. Working in both primary and pre-hospital care, you could find yourself on board ships or submarines all over the world, on shore, flying in helicopters or even winning yourself the coveted green beret of a Royal Marines Commando.

After completing my New Entry Medical Officers course, learning about trauma, diving, submarine, aviation and radiation medicine, and spending seven weeks in Initial Officer Training at Britannia Royal Naval College (BRNC), I returned to BRNC. I worked for four months in the medical centre providing primary care to the young officers and staff before deploying out to the Northern Arabian Gulf on a Royal Fleet Auxiliary ship. The only doctor in the area, with the nearest hospital a forty-minute helicopter ride away, I suddenly found myself solely responsible for the lives of both multinational forces and civilians. I treated patients in cabins on oil tankers, on oil platforms, on local fishing vessels and other naval vessels. Travelling by small patrol boat through rough seas or evacuating patients by helicopter suddenly becomes more challenging in the middle of the night!

I am privileged to be working as the Medical Officer to 45 Commando Royal Marines and will spend two years in a hugely varied role. Providing primary care, delivering training, acting as practice manager and ensuring the welfare of my medical staff are just some of my jobs whilst we are based in the UK. I am also preparing the whole unit for its next operational deployment to Afghanistan. Co-ordinating the vaccination of over 800 men and teaching half that number to become team medics both create their own unique challenges. This all continues alongside my own preparation for deployment where I will again be working in primary and pre-hospital care. Dealing with major trauma or mass casualty situations one day and sprained ankles the next.

So why did I join the Royal Navy and not the Army or the Royal Air Force? All three services offer similar medical cadetships, encourage physical fitness and teamwork through sport and adventure training, and provide competitive entry to specialist training. It is the breadth of experience to be gained from the Royal Navy that persuaded me. You could find yourself providing humanitarian assistance in the Caribbean, working at the cutting edge of diving or aviation medicine, supporting land operations with the Royal Marines or underwater on patrol in a submarine.

If you are robust enough, thrive on responsibility and challenges, remain calm under extreme pressure and are looking for truly unique career opportunities then why not consider becoming a Medical Officer in the Armed Forces?"

Profile: Dr Jemma Austin
MBChB DRCOG DFSRH MRCGP

Jemma is a GP in the RAF working out in Cyprus. She applied to Medical School knowing a medical career with a twist was what she wanted and joining the RAF as a doctor is how she has done it. Sponsorship by the RAF throughout her time at Bristol Medical School opened up many interesting options whilst she studied and beyond.

Jemma's Story

"I finally decided on medicine just before the UCAS deadlines loomed. I tried to get as much experience from different places as possible – serving meals at my local hospital, working in a respite home for multiple sclerosis sufferers, joining a pilgrim to Lourdes and even a few days at the local dentists. I had always been interested in the RAF and many of the skills and experiences I'd gained as an Air Cadet added substance to my UCAS application. Practical leadership experience, community involvement and a broad range of extra-curricular activity and commitment encouraged the interview offers.

Interviews were unique to each medical school in content of questioning and panel participants. My advice is to relax and feel confident in what you talk about – apart from the generic medical school stuff they want to find out who you are and what you're about – leads you've given them on your application form. Research anything you might be asked about medically. I knew nothing about multiple sclerosis as a diagnosis despite my work experience so after tripping over the tea trolley on the way in, continued to stumble through the interview at Sheffield (no offer unsurprisingly…). Try to consider any awkward questions that may come your way following your personal statement. During my Bristol interview I was challenged over my choice to join the Armed Forces. "Why should we train you as a doctor if you're never going to work for the NHS?" and "Aren't you going to get bored only dealing with young fit soldiers?" were asked. Looking back now, after 6 years of being a doctor in the RAF, I feel vindicated in my justified responses of 'definitely not!'

During my time at Bristol University I was sponsored by the RAF for my 5 year course. This ensured I remained financially buoyant throughout and left with minimal debt (see your local Armed Forces Career office or **www.raf.mod.uk/careers** if you want to know more about sponsorship and entry requirements). However, the best bit for me was the broadening of my university experience. I was a member of the University Air Squadron and had at least weekly involvement with a group of non-medics, a refreshing change when you didn't want to talk medicine the majority of the time. I also got many different opportunities like traveling to the Virgin Islands to assist the doctor on a sailing expedition, kayaking in France, learning to ski and generally having lots of fun (this has continued now qualified and I've recently been medically involved in trips to Argentina and Nepal). During my fourth year I got to spend a special study module in Washington DC with the US military medical school (USUHS). This was fantastic trauma training and the first time I got to experience medical provision in field conditions. I'm really glad the military experience came alongside my medical school experience.

Following house jobs I spent a couple of months learning to be an RAF Medical Officer at Royal Air Force College Cranwell and the RAF Centre of Aviation Medicine combined with an RAF Station placement to broaden my military medical experience. I then completed the full NHS GP vocational training program. We have to pass the same exams and assessments to the same standards as our NHS counterparts, often having to balance this with our military commitments like deployments to Afghanistan at the same time. There are no separate military hospitals now (bar the famous rehabilitation centre Headley Court where rehabilitation teams work hard to mend our injured Servicemen) but we do have units attached to large UK hospitals (MDHUs). This provides us with excellent training managing both military and a full range of NHS patients. We are well received and provide a lot of support and different skills to the NHS trusts we work within.

I'm currently a military GP living in Cyprus with a brilliant and interesting patient group. My daily clinic is broad and varied from pregnant women, unwell children, occupational health considerations with soldiers deploying to war zones, sports injuries to management of chronic conditions found anywhere in the UK. As a practice we provide emergency cover to our local area. This sees me attending the scene of accidents and serious illnesses in support of our medics. There is no service here like the UK's '999' so my emergency skills are kept very active; for the British Forces community we serve, *we are* their 'NHS'.

As I left medical school our clinical dean said 'medicine is your passport to the rest of the world'. This is the best bit of advice I could pass on to anyone. There are so many things you can do with a medical degree and I've chosen to support the Armed Forces by joining the RAF with mine. Once you're at medical school take every opportunity available, try new things, go to new places and you never know where it may lead you. If all goes well you're going to be a doctor for anywhere up to 45 years! That's a long, long time so have fun getting there. There really is no rush to become what you want to be and all your experiences along the way will develop you as an adult and a doctor. Good luck!"

"The future belongs to those who believe in the beauty of their dreams..."

Eleanor Roosevelt

Med School Final Thoughts

A medical degree opens the door to a huge range of enthralling and challenging careers, but at the same time demands an enormous amount of hard work and perseverance. Competition for places at medical school is as fierce as almost any other university degree. You will have to study harder and for more years than other students and once you qualify you face the prospect of many more years of training and exams before you make it to the top. It certainly is not for everyone but if you are reading this book there is a good chance that you are at least thinking that it might be for you and we hope to have given you an insight into some of the realities of the job. You owe it to yourself, however, to find out as much as you can by speaking to people from years above you at school who have gone on to medical school, begging and scrounging for any work experience that you can get and exhausting any contacts that you might have to confirm your decision.

Every day as a doctor there are new challenges to stimulate you, new techniques to master and an endless stream of fascinating people to meet, all grateful for your efforts to sort out their problems. There are unquestionably many less stressful ways to make a good living, but if you are going into medicine for the right reasons there really is nothing else that could give you this level of job satisfaction. Those of us who are fortunate enough to experience this could not imagine doing any other kind of work. We would like to wish you the best of luck and hope that you get the same sense of fulfilment wherever you may end up.

Good Luck!

Dr Ross Muir & Hélena Gresty

Appendix 1

Undergraduate Medicine Courses

University of Aberdeen
www.abdn.ac.uk/medicine-dentistry
- 5 year course
- Relatively small school
- Opportunity to undertake an additional 1-year intercalated degree
- Quota: home (162) and international students (13)
- UK CAT required
- Systems-based and problem-orientated approach to teaching (fully integrated). Students understand the science that underpins disease, clinical method, diagnosis and treatment. Also use CAL (computer aided learning). Students are encouraged to explore concepts for themselves and to utilise the excellent facilities available.
- Remote and Rural Option (Years 4 and 5) – unusual selling point. Placements all over Highlands and islands.

The University of Birmingham
www.medicine.bham.ac.uk
- 5 year course
- Independent and self-directed learning
- Extensive library and information technology-based material
- Systems based in first 2 years

Brighton and Sussex Medical School
www.bsms.ac.uk
- 5 years
- Small and personal medical school
- Opportunity to undertake an additional 1-year intercalated degree

- Traditional lecture-based learning is supported by a skills-based and problem-solving approach, with group sessions and strong IT support.
- Totally integrated approach - real clinical problems in clinical settings from the start
- Major component of year 4 is an individual in-depth research study

University of Bristol
www.bristol.ac.uk/fmd
- Standard 5 year course
- Intercalate an extra year in order to study for an Honours BSc degree
- 2 years preclinical with some patient contact
- Strength in research-informed teaching – keen on European Credit Transfer Scheme. You will have the opportunity to spend a period of 3-6 months at a participating European Medical School in Year 3, and receive credit for academic work successfully undertaken there.

Pre-medical entry:
- 6 year course for candidates who did not do at least 2 sciences at A-level
- As above but with extra first year in Chemistry, Physics, and Anatomical Science

University Of Cambridge
www.med.cam.ac.uk
- 6 year course
- BMAT exam & college application required
- Old-school traditional, 3 year preclinical including BA degree
- Standard 3 year clinical course (50% transfer to London/Oxford)
- **MB PhD programme** enables students who are planning a career in academic medicine to intercalate three years of research with their clinical training

Cardiff University
www.medicine.cf.ac.uk

- 5 year course
- Integrated curriculum, traditional learning methods with aspects of a problem-centred approach

Foundation course:

- For students who have demonstrated high academic potential and have non-science subjects or fewer than 2 sciences at A-level
- One year modular programme – students study twelve modules alongside students from other science disciplines

University of Dundee
www.dundee.ac.uk/medschool

- 5 year course
- Approximately 100 core clinical problems provide a vital focus for learning (PBL)

Pre medical year:

- Designed for very able applicants who have a predominantly non-science background

University Of East Anglia
www.uea.ac.uk/med

- 5 year course
- Problem Based Learning (PBL) structure
- Small group sessions supported by whole class discussions, lectures, and seminars
- Systems based approach right through to final year

University Of Edinburgh
www.ed.ac.uk

- 5 year course
- Intercalated Honours programme available
- Leading position in world medicine since the early 18th century

- Teaching mainly based on the systems of the human body – cover each twice in preclinical and clinical
- Wide range of teaching techniques with 2 years preclinical

University of Glasgow
www.gla.ac.uk/medicine
- 5 year course
- Problem-based learning, integrated and systems based
- Vocational Studies runs for one session each week, throughout the first three years

Hull York Medical School
www.hyms.ac.uk
- 5 year course
- Intercalated year option in York or elsewhere
- 2 years PBL (contact time is 15 hours per week), online virtual learning environment, patient contact from week two of the course
- Course is new and unfettered by past educational methods

Imperial College London
www1.imperial.ac.uk/medicine
- 6 year course
- BSc science year included in year 4
- Evidence-based medicine is a fundamental component of the MBBS programme, as is direct contact
- Varied teaching styles, including lectures and PBL
- First hospital-based clinical experience in year 2, with some patient contact before

Keele University
www.keele.ac.uk/health/schoolofmedicine
- 5 year course
- Opportunity for intercalated degree/ masters

- Innovative highly-integrated modern medical curriculum, which includes problem-based learning. 20 hours contact time.
- Smaller group sizes than most unis

Health Foundation Year: for non science A-level graduates

King's College London (University of London)
www.kcl.ac.uk/schools/medicine
- 5 year course
- Intercalated BSc an option
- Big school
- Full integration of basic medical science and clinical teaching – patient contact in week 1
- Students are encouraged to take responsibility for their own learning

University of Leeds
www.leeds.ac.uk/medicine
- 5 year course
- Intercalated degree option
- 3 years of primarily preclinical with essential clinical skills
- Emphasis is put on self-directed learning
- New MBChB Curriculum for 2010

University of Leicester
www.le.ac.uk/sm/le
- 5 year course
- Intercalated degree option
- Highly integrated, both 'horizontally' so that disciplines within medicine are learned together, and 'vertically' in that clinical work and relevance are introduced from the beginning
- 2 ½ years preclinical
- Meet patients very early on in your study

The University of Liverpool
www.liv.ac.uk/medicine
- 5 year course
- Intercalated degree option
- Some lectures, lots of self directed study and PBL heavy
- Clinical contact with patients occurs in the second semester of the first year

The University of Liverpool Medicine (based at Lancaster University)
www.liv.ac.uk
- 5 year course
- Same curriculum as Liverpool course but delivered in Lancaster
- Clinical Anatomy Learning Centre (CALC)

The University of Manchester
www.medicine.manchester.ac.uk
- 5 year course
- Intercalated option
- European Studies option - weekly tuition in a selected language with the option to study in a European country
- PBL based, approx. 16 hours of classes a week
- Early clinical contact

Foundation course:
- 6 year foundation course offered covering foundations of basic biomedical sciences including chemistry, human biology and statistics

Newcastle University
mbbs.ncl.ac.uk
- 5 year course
- First 2 years either in Newcastle or Durham's Queen's Campus at Stockton
- Systems modules plus clinical contact via a GP

The University of Nottingham
www.nottingham.ac.uk/mhs
- 5 years, obtain a Bachelor of Medical Sciences (BMedSci) degree after three years
- Research component of the BMedSci degree provides students with excellent experience in research
- Relies on e-resources for teaching and assessment
- Early interaction with patients starting within the first few weeks of the course
- Anatomy continues to be taught using whole body dissection

University of Oxford
www.medsci.ox.ac.uk
- 6 year course
- Academic skills and scientific knowledge emphasised
- 3 years preclinical concentrating on basic sciences
- Lecture/practical based
- Clinical is further 3 years, in Oxford or can transfer to either London or Cambridge

Peninsula College of Medicine & Dentistry
www.pms.ac.uk
- 5 year course
- Centred around patient exposure for students and small group work
- Clinical skills training starts in your first week
- First 2 years students learn science within a clinical context
- Structured around the human life cycle
- 48 core cases in Years 3 and 4 covering common conditions

Queen Mary, University of London
www.smd.qmul.ac.uk
- 5 year course
- Integrated curriculum so start seeing patients from the first term

- Problem Based Learning (PBL) with some lectures

Queen's University Belfast
www.qub.ac.uk/schools/mdbs
- 5 year course
- Intercalated option
- Can leave after 3 years with BMedSc ordinary degree
- Integrated, body systems based and student centred approach
- Little didactic teaching
- Particular emphasis on development of clinical skills

The University of Sheffield
www.sheffield.ac.uk/medicine
- 5 year course
- Intercalated option
- Variety of teaching approaches
- 2 years of systems based preclinical sciences with three weeks Intensive Clinical Experience (ICE)

Foundation course:
- 6 year foundation course - pre-medical Science Foundation Course is a modified Access to Science course

University of Southampton
www.som.soton.ac.uk
- 5 year course
- Intercalated masters degree an option
- Plans to award BMedSciences degree after year 4
- Traditional and modern teaching methods
- Integrated, systems based for 2 years, clinical contact in first few weeks

BM6 Programme:
- 6 years
- Offered to applicants who would not previously have been able to get places, such first generation applicants to higher education;

those whose parent/ guardian receives means-tested benefits, or the student themselves receive benefits; in receipt of Educational Maintenance Award; or if living in a postcode in lower 20% of Index of Multiple Deprivation
- CCC A-level requirement
- £1000 bursary in first year
- Extensive pastoral support
- First year of basic science to equip students with relevant knowledge to join standard course

University of St Andrews
medicine.st-andrews.ac.uk
- 3 years BSc course
- Preclinical - must then go on to complete further 3 years clinical at another Scottish University or Manchester (select at time of admission)
- Small school
- Year 1 basic preclinical sciences
- Series of patient-centred workshops that are designed to demonstrate how you can apply your scientific knowledge
- Year 3 Honours level project and the Applied Medicine module

St Georges Medical School
www.sgul.ac.uk
- 5 year course
- Intercalated option
- 2 years clinical science
- Integrative 3rd year
- Case based learning plus lectures and small group

6 year foundation degree:
- Extra 1-year course for those who do not have the academic qualifications normally required for medicine. Progress onto 5 year course if attain a sufficient standard

University College London (University of London)
www.ucl.ac.uk/slms

- 6 year course
- Award of MBBS and an additional degree of Bachelor of Science (BSc)
- Central London location means teaching in well-respected hospitals
- Research-led teaching from current leaders in basic medical science and clinical medicine
- First 2 years preclinical lecture and lab based with some CAL, PBL and self-directed learning
- Anatomy still taught by dissection and prosection

Appendix 2

Graduate Medicine Courses

University of Birmingham
www.medicine.bham.ac.uk
- 4 year course
- 1 year case-based plus GP
- 3 years hospital based
- Expert lectures, small group teaching and supervised clinical experience

University of Bristol
www.bristol.ac.uk/fmd/gradschool
- 4 year course
- Transitional first year of the course aims to build on your existing knowledge of the medical sciences
- Last 3 years with regular track

University of Cambridge
www.medschl.cam.ac.uk/education/courses/cgc
- 4 year course
- Students follow the same core medical sciences course in the first four and a half terms as those on the standard pre-clinical course, and take the Second MB exams. They also do 1½ days clinical work. They then complete clinical studies during their last year in West Suffolk, although not at Addenbrooke's.

Imperial College London
www1.imperial.ac.uk/medicine/teaching/undergraduate/ge
- 4 year course

- First year supplementing the basic knowledge to take you to the same level as those who have completed the first two years of the six-year undergraduate MBBS course
- Much of this involves self-directed study
- Join normal trackers for years 3, 5 and 6

Keele University
www.keele.ac.uk/health/schoolofmedicine
- 4 year course
- Biomedical graduates enter directly into year 2 of the standard course

Kings College London
www.kcl.ac.uk/schools/medicine
- 4 year course
- Full integration of medical science and clinical teaching.
- Join normal track for years 3-5

University of Leicester
www.le.ac.uk/sm/le
- 4 year course

University of Liverpool
www.liv.ac.uk/medicine
- 4 year course
- Extended year 1 – sit the same examinations as students at the end of their 2nd year
- Same as normal course for last 3 years

Newcastle University
mbbs.ncl.ac.uk
- 4 year course
- Fits content of first 2 years of standard course into 45 weeks.

- Last 3 years the same as standard course

The University of Nottingham
www.nottingham.ac.uk/gem
- 4 year course
- 18-month Pre Clinical programme structured around problem-based learning (PBL). Based at the purpose built Medical School on the Derby City General Hospital site
- Non-science graduates usually account for 30-40% of the intake

University of Oxford
www.medsci.ox.ac.uk
- 4 year course
- First year PBL and self-directed with clinical experience at GPs
- Second year integrates with normal course, plus extra work

Queen Mary, University of London
www.smd.qmul.ac.uk
- 4 year course
- First year of study is run jointly with City University as a multi-professional programme, where medical students join an equal number of graduates who are on accelerated programmes leading to qualifications in other health professions
- In year 2 students join undergraduate students for clinical studies

University of Southampton
www.som.soton.ac.uk
- 4 year course
- PBL based but with additional lectures and clinical experience for first 2 years
- Join normal track for last 2 years

St Georges Medical School
www.sgul.ac.uk
- 4 year course
- Open to graduates of all subjects
- Problem based learning
- Last 2 years same as normal course

Swansea University
www.gemedicine.swan.ac.uk
- 4 year course
- Fully integrated, case centred lectures plus small group discussion
- Clinical placements without specific learning objectives or assessments

The University of Warwick
www2.warwick.ac.uk/fac/med/study/ugr
- 4 year course
- Largest graduate entry programme in the UK
- 18 months lectures, small group and some clinical exposure
- One to one student to consultant pairing during clinical attachments